Longman
English Interactive 2

Activity and
Resource Book

Michael Rost

Longman

Longman English Interactive 2
Activity and Resource Book

Acknowledgments
We wish to thank the following users, reviewers, and piloters of *Longman English Interactive* for contributing ideas toward the development of the Activity and Resource Book:

Elizabeth Ianotti, Jennifer Benichou, *LaGuardia Community College*
Banu Yaylali, Kathy Biache, *Miami-Dade Community College*
Alfredo Rodriguez, *KPMG Mexico*
Julie Fanara, *Howard Community College*

The author wishes to thank Nancy Blodgett, Lynn Contrucci, Hugo Loyola, Irene Frankel, and Sherry Preiss for their guidance and support during the development of this activity book. The author also wishes to thank the entire Pearson multimedia team for their ongoing development of *Longman English Interactive*.

Pearson Education, 10 Bank Street, White Plains, NY 10606

Vice president, adult and higher ed publishing: Sherry Preiss
Associate project manager: Nancy Blodgett
Senior development editor: Debbie Sistino
Associate development editor: Pamela Kohn
Executive managing editor: Linda Moser
Production editor: Lynn Contrucci
Senior art director: Elizabeth Carlson
Executive producer: Ken Volcjak
Multimedia production editor: Jennifer Raspiller
Vice president, marketing: Kate McLoughlin
Senior product manager: Hugo Loyola
Senior manufacturing buyer: Dave Dickey
Cover design: Inez Sovjani
Cover photo: Mark Harmel/Stone (Getty Images)
Text design: Quorum Creative Services
Text composition: TSI Graphics
Photo credits: **page 11** (*left*) © Piecework Productions/Getty Images; (*center*) © Hans Neleman/The Image Bank; (*right*) © LWA-Dann Tardif/Corbis; **page 84** (*left*) © Yellow Dog Productions/Getty Images; (*center left*) © Jerry Koontz/Image Stock Imagery, Inc.; (*center right*) © Stephen Shugerman/Getty Images; (right) © Peter Mason/Getty Images; **page 91** (*top*) © Mike Powell/Getty Images; (*bottom*) © Silvestre Machado/Getty Images; **page 96** © Todd Gipstein/Getty Images; **page 107** © Toby Melville/Reuters/Corbis
Illustrations: Brian Hughes

LONGMAN ON THE **WEB**

Longman.com offers online resources for teachers and students. Access our Companion Websites, our online catalog, and our local offices around the world.

Visit us at **longman.com**.

ISBN: 0-13-152087-3

Printed in the United States of America
1 2 3 4 5 6 7 8 9 10–WC–09 08 07 06 05

Contents

Scope and Sequence

Module	Function	Pronunciation	Grammar	Reading/Writing
A.1 Do I Know You? Theme: Introductions	Introducing yourself, talking about yourself	• Sentence stress • Intonation for clarification	• Statements and *yes/no* questions with *be* • Simple present tense: statements and *yes/no* questions • Short answers to *yes/no* questions	Article/Advertisement
A.2 Somebody New Theme: People/ Personalities	Introducing people, describing people	• Word stress • Contractions	• Adjectives • Statements with *be* vs. *have* • Information questions	News article/ Biography
A.3 A Quick Lunch Theme: Food	Ordering food, talking about quantities	• *Wh-* question stress and intonation • Intonation in questions with *or*	• Count and non-count nouns • Quantifiers: *some* and *any* • Quantifiers: *how much, how many, a little, a few*	Recipe/Letter
A.4 What a Weekend! Theme: Activities, entertainment	Asking/talking about personal activities, making small talk	• Shortened phrases: *didja* • City names around the world	• The past tense of *be*: *was* and *were* • Simple past: regular verbs • Simple past: irregular verbs	Brochure/Letter
A.5 Working Smart Theme: Technology, computers	Giving instructions, asking for instructions	• The sound [h] • Shortened phrases: *hafta* and *hasta*	• *Can, should,* and *have to* • Imperatives: giving instructions • Adverbs of manner	FAQs/Email
B.1 Feeling Down Theme: Health	Sympathizing, talking about health	• Simple present verb endings [s], [z], [iz] • The sound [ɚ]	• Simple present and present continuous • Stative verbs • Asking for clarification	Article/Letter
B.2 Late Again Theme: Transportation	Giving directions, asking for directions	• Numbers in street addresses • The sounds [l] and [r]	• Prepositions of location • Directions and locations • Exclamations: expressing emotions	Email/Fax

Module	Function	Pronunciation	Grammar	Reading/Writing
B.3 Weekend Plans Theme: Invitations	Asking about/ confirming plans, making suggestions	• The sound [l] and contractions with *will* • Shortened phrases: *gonna*	• Future: *will* and *be going to* • *May* and *might* • Exclamations: expressions for special occasions	Web page/Invitation
B.4 Excellent Choice! Theme: Responsibilities	Talking about activities and events	• The sounds [s] and [tʃ] • Phrasal verb stress	• Expressions with *do* and *make* • Expressions with *get* • Definite and indefinite articles	Article/Email
B.5 Sound Advice Theme: Relationships, friends, dating	Asking for/giving advice	• Stress in sentences with *but* • Shortened phrases: *wanna*	• Gerunds and infinitives • Giving advice • *Too* and *enough*	Article/Letter
C.1 Welcome Back Theme: Travel/travel problems	Reporting, responding/ sympathizing, talking about past events	• Past tense endings [t], [d], [id] • Word stress	• Past continuous • Review of the past tense • Past tense sequences	Letter/Letter
C.2 A Better Place Theme: Housing	Showing, responding, comparing	• Noun, adverb, and adjective stress • The sound [s] and *s*-blends	• Comparative adjectives • Similarities and differences: *as . . . as* • Comparing nouns	Advertisement/Email
C.3 Somewhere Around Here Theme: Background, geography	Describing places, comparing places	• Stress for understanding • Plural noun endings [s], [z], [iz]	• Superlatives • Definite and indefinite articles and no article • Review of pronouns, possessive nouns, and possessive adjectives	Advertisement/Email
C.4 It's Spicy! Theme: Culture, new things	Asking about/ explaining cultural items	• Stress in noun compounds • Stress in sentences with *that* and *who*	• Review of questions • Relative pronouns and relative clauses • Tag questions	Article/Letter
C.5 You Gotta Do It! Theme: News	Talking about news, talking about experiences	• Shortened phrases: *gotta* and *oughtta* • Shortened phrases: *havya* and *arya*	• Present perfect • Present perfect and past tense • Review of tenses	Article/Thank you letter

To the Teacher

About *Longman English Interactive*

Longman English Interactive is a comprehensive multimedia course that lets students work at their own pace on a range of language learning activities. *Longman English Interactive 2* consists of software (two CD-ROM disks) that students use in a computer learning lab or on their own computers. Each unit is based on a short video story, with closely linked exercises for listening, speaking, grammar, pronunciation, vocabulary, and reading development. Each unit of the CD-ROM course provides up to 4 hours of self-paced instruction employing extensive video, audio, and animated graphics, and including interactive exercises, review quizzes, and immediate feedback.

About the *Longman English Interactive Activity and Resource Book*

This *Activity and Resource Book* is designed to serve as a personal or classroom resource for learners and as a management tool for teachers and course coordinators who are using the *Longman English Interactive* multimedia software.

- Simple screenshots help students quickly learn how to use the software.
- Progress Checks for each unit enable students to keep a record of completed activities and scores on the review quizzes in the CD-ROM course.
- Additional listening tasks let students review the course audio segments. Each *Activity and Resource Book* includes an audio CD.
- Vocabulary reviews offer students new ways of remembering key words and phrases from each unit.
- Expanded grammar exercises for each grammar point allow students to consolidate learning.
- Application Activities provide multiple ways for students to apply what they have learned in realistic ways.

This *Activity and Resource Book* can be used as a self-access learning guide or as a classroom text for students who are using *Longman English Interactive*. Best used after completing each unit of the *Longman English Interactive* CD-ROM course, students can use the *Activity and Resource Book* at home, in the computer lab, or in the classroom. Students can complete each exercise (Listening, Vocabulary, and Grammar) on their own or with a study partner or group and consult the Grammar Explanations at the end of each unit of the *Activity and Resource Book* as needed. They can also refer to the Audioscript and check their own answers with the Answer Key at the back of the *Activity and Resource Book*.

Classroom follow-up will help students consolidate their learning and allow for additional personal attention. As time permits, teachers can also guide the students with the selection of one or more Application Activities which wrap up each unit. Teachers or course coordinators should be sure to monitor students' Progress Checks, to confirm that students are completing each section of the CD-ROM course and are showing ample progress on the review quizzes at the end of each unit.

For additional classroom communication activities, the *Longman English Interactive Communication Companion* is available as both 15 downloadable documents (PDFs) in the CD-ROM course or as a full 64-page, four-color book. The *Longman English Interactive 2 Teacher's Guide*, available for download on the Longman website (www.longman.com/multimedia), provides further suggestions for classroom activities and homework assignments.

The following chart gives an overview of how the sections of the *Longman English Interactive Activity and Resource Book* correspond to the CD-ROM course.

CD-ROM course section	*Activity and Resource Book* corresponding section
Listening Listening Challenge (Extended Listening)	Listening Exercise A (with Audio CD): a new activity with the same extracts
Listening Challenge (More Listening)	Listening Exercise B (with Audio CD): a new activity with the same extract
Speaking (Role Play)	
Grammar 1	Grammar 1: a review of the grammar point in a new context
Grammar 2	Grammar 2: a review of the grammar point in a new context
Grammar 3	Grammar 3: a review of the grammar point in a new context
Vocabulary	Vocabulary: review of vocabulary items in a new context
Pronunciation	
Reading	
Review Quiz Unit Summary	Application Activities

To the Student

Welcome to *Longman English Interactive 2*. This *Activity and Resource Book* will help you with the course.

After you complete each unit of the CD-ROM course, review the unit by doing the exercises in this *Activity and Resource Book*.

Here is a study guide for using the CD-ROM course.

Start at the Course Home.

- Click on the **Orientation** button to download a PDF file with detailed information about using the CD-ROM course.
- Click on the **Course Overview** button to start the course.

As you go through each unit in the CD-ROM course, try these study tips.

Listening

- Watch each video 3 times.
- Use the "pause" button, if necessary.
- Try the exercises. Check your answers. Click on 🄴 for an explanation.
- Check the transcript after you finish.

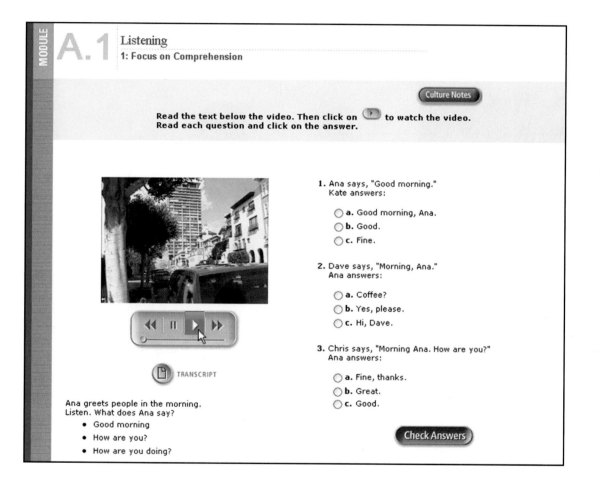

Speaking

- Choose one role. Click on the picture of the person.

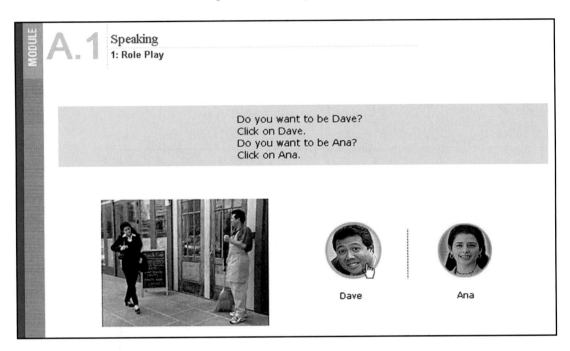

- Select "Show example" or "Show example with blanks."
- Click on ▶ to start the role play. Each time you see a speech bubble, record your voice. Speak loudly and clearly.

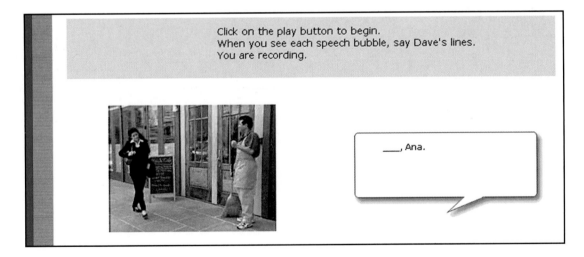

- Play back your voice. Compare with the character.
- Try again. This time, select "No example." Record and play back.
- Now choose the other role. Practice again.

Grammar

- Listen to the grammar presentations.
- Watch as the words grow, move, and change color. Think about the grammar.
- Try the exercises. Check your answers. Click on 📧 for an explanation.

MODULE

A.1 Grammar
1: Greetings and Responses

Click on ▶ below the Grammar Coach. Then click on each ▶ to hear the explanations and examples.

1. In the morning, we say:

Good morning

Morning

Hi

or

Hello

2. In the afternoon, we say:

Good afternoon

Hi

Pronunciation

- Listen to both pronunciation sections.
- Record your voice. Compare with the model.

MODULE

A.1 Pronunciation
1.1: Intonation: Good Morning, Good-bye

Click here: 🔊 . Listen to the intonation: "Good MORNing." Compare your recording to the model.

Click on ▶ below to listen to the model.
Click on 🎤 below to record your voice. Click again to stop the recording.
Click on ▶ below to listen to your recording.
Click on ▶ below to listen to the model again.

Play the Model	Record/Play Your Recording
1. ▶ Good MORNing.	🎤 ▶
2. ▶ Good afterNOON.	🎤 ▶
3. ▶ Good EVEning.	🎤 ▶

Review Quiz

- Take the review quiz for each unit.
- Check your score. Review the necessary skills if you have any difficulties.

Progress Report

Unit A.1 Review Quiz

Learner's name:

Score: 84%

Skill	Number correct/number of items
Listening comprehension	7/8
Listening for language	9/9
Grammar (Greetings and responses)	7/10
Grammar (Farewells and responses)	5/7

When you use this *Resource and Activity Book*, spend between 45 and 90 minutes on each unit.

Progress Checks

Record your progress for each unit of the CD-ROM course. Make a check (✓) for each activity that you completed. Write your scores for the Review Quiz. (5 minutes)

Listening

Use the Audio CD and do the exercises. (20 minutes)

Vocabulary

Do the Vocabulary exercises. (10 minutes)

Grammar

Review the Grammar Explanations. (10 minutes)

Do the Grammar exercises. (20 minutes)

Answer Key

Check your answers on pages 117–124. (5 minutes)

Application Activities

Choose one or two activities. Start the activities. (20 minutes—You will need more time for some activities.)

When possible, study with your classmates and your teacher. You can learn a lot of English with *Longman English Interactive*! Have fun using the course.

Name _____ Date _____

 **PROGRESS CHECKS**

A.1 Do I Know You?

As you complete each section of the CD-ROM course, make a check (✔). Write your scores for the Review Quiz.

Listening
_____ Focus on comprehension
_____ Focus on language

Speaking
_____ Chris's role
_____ Sam's role

Grammar
_____ 1. Statements and *yes/no* questions with *be*
_____ 2. The simple present tense: Statements and *yes/no* questions
_____ 3. Short answers to *yes/no* questions

Vocabulary
_____ Jobs (Your time _____ : _____)

Listening Challenge
_____ Extended listening
_____ More listening: Ana calls for a taxi

Pronunciation
_____ 1. Sentence stress
_____ 2. Intonation for clarification

Reading: Internet Job Website
_____ Focus on vocabulary
_____ Focus on comprehension

Review Quiz	Score
Listening comprehension	_____ / 9
Listening for language	_____ / 9
Grammar 1	_____ / 10
Grammar 2	_____ / 5
Grammar 3	_____ / 3
Vocabulary	_____ / 5
Pronunciation	_____ / 4
Reading	_____ / 8
Objective 1: Introduce yourself	_____ %
Objective 2: Talk about yourself	_____ %
Objective 3: Talk about others	_____ %

A.2 Somebody New

As you complete each section of the CD-ROM course, make a check (✔). Write your scores for the Review Quiz.

Listening
_____ Focus on comprehension
_____ Focus on language

Speaking
_____ Laura's role
_____ Luis's role

Grammar
_____ 1. Adjectives
_____ 2. Statements with *be* and *have*
_____ 3. Information questions

Vocabulary
_____ Describing people (Your time _____ : _____)

Listening Challenge
_____ Extended listening
_____ More listening: A new colleague

Pronunciation
_____ 1. Word stress
_____ 2. Contractions

Reading: Women in the News
_____ Focus on vocabulary
_____ Focus on comprehension

Review Quiz	Score
Listening comprehension	_____ / 10
Listening for language	_____ / 8
Grammar 1	_____ / 12
Grammar 2	_____ / 6
Vocabulary	_____ / 5
Pronunciation	_____ / 4
Reading	_____ / 8
Objective 1: Introduce people	_____ %
Objective 2: Describe people	_____ %
Objective 3: Ask about people	_____ %

PROGRESS CHECKS

A.3 A Quick Lunch

As you complete each section of the CD-ROM course, make a check (✓). Write your scores for the Review Quiz.

Listening
_____ Focus on comprehension
_____ Focus on language

Speaking
_____ Emi's role
_____ Dave's role

Grammar
_____ 1. Count and non-count nouns
_____ 2. Quantifiers: *Some* and *any*
_____ 3. Quantifiers: *How much, how many, a little, a few*

Vocabulary
_____ Meals (Your time _____ : _____)

Listening Challenge
_____ Extended listening
_____ More listening: Telephone order

Pronunciation
_____ 1. *Wh-* question stress and intonation
_____ 2. Intonation in questions with *or*

Reading: Pancakes
_____ Focus on vocabulary
_____ Focus on comprehension

Review Quiz	Score
Listening comprehension	_____ / 10
Listening for language	_____ / 8
Grammar 1	_____ / 11
Grammar 2	_____ / 5
Grammar 3	_____ / 2
Vocabulary	_____ / 5
Pronunciation	_____ / 4
Reading	_____ / 8
Objective 1: Order food and drinks	_____ %
Objective 2: Ask about choices	_____ %
Objective 3: Read about food	_____ %

A.4 What a Weekend!

As you complete each section of the CD-ROM course, make a check (✓). Write your scores for the Review Quiz.

Listening
_____ Focus on comprehension
_____ Focus on language

Speaking
_____ Ana's role
_____ Chris's role

Grammar
_____ 1. The past tense of *be: Was* and *were*
_____ 2. The simple past tense: Regular verbs
_____ 3. The simple past tense: Irregular verbs

Vocabulary
_____ Traveling (Your time _____ : _____)

Listening Challenge
_____ Extended listening
_____ More listening: Train schedule

Pronunciation
_____ 1. Shortened phrases: *Didja*
_____ 2. City names around the world

Reading: Study and Travel
_____ Focus on vocabulary
_____ Focus on comprehension

Review Quiz	Score
Listening comprehension	_____ / 9
Listening for language	_____ / 9
Grammar 1	_____ / 12
Grammar 2	_____ / 6
Vocabulary	_____ / 5
Pronunciation	_____ / 3
Reading	_____ / 8
Objective 1: Talk about past activities	_____ %
Objective 2: Talk about personal activities and interests	_____ %
Objective 3: Read about educational tours	_____ %

PROGRESS CHECKS

A.5 Working Smart

As you complete each section of the CD-ROM course, make a check (✓). Write your scores for the Review Quiz.

Listening
_____ Focus on comprehension
_____ Focus on language

Speaking
_____ Laura's role
_____ Frankie's role

Grammar
_____ 1. *Can, should,* and *have to*
_____ 2. Imperatives: Giving instructions
_____ 3. Adverbs of manner

Vocabulary
_____ Using a computer (Your time ____:____)

Listening Challenge
_____ Extended listening
_____ More listening: Help desk

Pronunciation
_____ 1. Focus on sounds
_____ 2. Shortened phrases: *Hafta* and *hasta*

Reading: Find Answers
_____ Focus on vocabulary
_____ Focus on comprehension

Review Quiz	**Score**
Listening comprehension	_____ / 10
Listening for language	_____ / 8
Grammar 1	_____ / 8
Grammar 2	_____ / 4
Grammar 3	_____ / 6
Vocabulary	_____ / 5
Pronunciation	_____ / 3
Reading	_____ / 8
Objective 1: Give instructions	_____ %
Objective 2: Ask about instructions	_____ %
Objective 3: Read and ask for instructions	_____ %

B.1 Feeling Down

As you complete each section of the CD-ROM course, make a check (✓). Write your scores for the Review Quiz.

Listening
_____ Focus on comprehension
_____ Focus on language

Speaking
_____ Emi's role
_____ The doctor's role

Grammar
_____ 1. The simple present tense and the present continuous
_____ 2. Stative verbs
_____ 3. Asking for clarification: Review of questions

Vocabulary
_____ Feeling sick (Your time ____:____)

Listening Challenge
_____ Extended listening
_____ More listening: Appointment

Pronunciation
_____ 1. Simple present verb endings
_____ 2. Focus on sounds

Reading: From Stress to Relaxation
_____ Focus on vocabulary
_____ Focus on comprehension

Review Quiz	**Score**
Listening comprehension	_____ / 8
Listening for language	_____ / 10
Grammar 1	_____ / 6
Grammar 2	_____ / 9
Grammar 3	_____ / 3
Vocabulary	_____ / 5
Pronunciation	_____ / 3
Reading	_____ / 8
Objective 1: Talk about health	_____ %
Objective 2: Ask for and give advice	_____ %

⊙ PROGRESS CHECKS

B.2 Late Again

As you complete each section of the CD-ROM course, make a check (✓). Write your scores for the Review Quiz.

Listening	
_____ Focus on comprehension	
_____ Focus on language	
Speaking	
_____ Luis's role	
_____ Laura's role	
Grammar	
_____ 1. Prepositions of location	
_____ 2. Directions and locations	
_____ 3. Exclamations: Expressing emotions	
Vocabulary	
_____ Giving directions (Your time _____ : _____)	
Listening Challenge	
_____ Extended listening	
_____ More listening: Directions to Civic Arena	
Pronunciation	
_____ 1. Numbers in street addresses	
_____ 2. Focus on sounds	
Reading: Email from Kent	
_____ Focus on vocabulary	
_____ Focus on comprehension	

Review Quiz	Score
Listening comprehension	_____ / 8
Listening for language	_____ / 10
Grammar 1	_____ / 6
Grammar 2	_____ / 6
Grammar 3	_____ / 6
Vocabulary	_____ / 5
Pronunciation	_____ / 3
Reading	_____ / 8
Objective 1: Ask for directions	_____ %
Objective 2: Give directions	_____ %

B.3 Weekend Plans

As you complete each section of the CD-ROM course, make a check (✓). Write your scores for the Review Quiz.

Listening	
_____ Focus on comprehension	
_____ Focus on language	
Speaking	
_____ Ana's role	
_____ Chris's role	
Grammar	
_____ 1. Future: *Will* and *be going to*	
_____ 2. *May* and *might*	
_____ 3. Exclamations: Expressions for special occasions	
Vocabulary	
_____ Parties (Your time _____ : _____)	
Listening Challenge	
_____ Extended listening	
_____ More listening: Jin's message	
Pronunciation	
_____ 1. The sound /l/ and contractions with *will*	
_____ 2. Shortened phrases: *Gonna*	
Reading: Party Invitations	
_____ Focus on vocabulary	
_____ Focus on comprehension	

Review Quiz	Score
Listening comprehension	_____ / 9
Listening for language	_____ / 9
Grammar 1	_____ / 9
Grammar 2	_____ / 3
Grammar 3	_____ / 4
Vocabulary	_____ / 5
Reading	_____ / 8
Objective 1: Talk about future plans and ideas . . .	_____ %
Objective 2: Ask for and give suggestions	_____ %
Objective 3: Read an invitation	_____ %

PROGRESS CHECKS

B.4 Excellent Choice!

As you complete each section of the CD-ROM course, make a check (✓). Write your scores for the Review Quiz.

Listening	**Review Quiz** **Score**
_____ Focus on comprehension	Listening comprehension . . . . _____ / 9
_____ Focus on language	Listening for language . . . . _____ / 8
Speaking	Grammar 1 . . . . _____ / 5
_____ Paul's role	Grammar 2 . . . . _____ / 4
_____ Frankie's role	Grammar 3 . . . . _____ / 9
Grammar	Vocabulary . . . . _____ / 5
_____ 1. Expressions with _do_ and _make_	Pronunciation . . . . _____ / 3
_____ 2. Expressions with _get_	Reading . . . . _____ / 8
_____ 3. Definite and indefinite articles	
Vocabulary	Objective 1: Make suggestions . . . . _____ %
_____ Kinds of stores (Your time _____ : _____)	Objective 2: Give instructions . . . . _____ %
Listening Challenge	Objective 3: Read about the history of
_____ Extended listening	something . . . . _____ %
_____ More listening: Dave orders supplies	
Pronunciation	
_____ 1. Focus on sounds	
_____ 2. Phrasal verb stress	
Reading: The History of Ice Cream	
_____ Focus on vocabulary	
_____ Focus on comprehension	

B.5 Sound Advice

As you complete each section of the CD-ROM course, make a check (✓). Write your scores for the Review Quiz.

Listening	**Review Quiz** **Score**
_____ Focus on comprehension	Listening comprehension . . . . _____ / 9
_____ Focus on language	Listening for language . . . . _____ / 9
Speaking	Grammar 1 . . . . _____ / 7
_____ Emi's role	Grammar 2 . . . . _____ / 6
_____ Maggie's role	Grammar 3 . . . . _____ / 3
Grammar	Vocabulary . . . . _____ / 5
_____ 1. Gerunds and infinitives	Pronunciation . . . . _____ / 3
_____ 2. Giving advice	Reading . . . . _____ / 8
_____ 3. _Too_ and _enough_	
Vocabulary	Objective 1: Ask for and give advice . . . . . . _____ %
_____ Going out (Your time _____ : _____)	Objective 2: Talk about something you want
Listening Challenge	to do . . . . _____ %
_____ Extended listening	
_____ More listening: School announcement	
Pronunciation	
_____ 1. Sentence stress with _but_	
_____ 2. Shortened phrases: _Wanna_	
Reading: Advice Column	
_____ Focus on vocabulary	
_____ Focus on comprehension	

⊙ PROGRESS CHECKS

C.1 Welcome Back

As you complete each section of the CD-ROM course, make a check (✓). Write your scores for the Review Quiz.

Listening
____ Focus on comprehension
____ Focus on language

Speaking
____ Ana's role
____ Kate's role

Grammar
____ 1. The past continuous
____ 2. Review of the past tense
____ 3. Past tense sequences

Vocabulary
____ Air travel (Your time ____:____)

Listening Challenge
____ Extended listening
____ More listening: Phone call about a lost bag

Pronunciation
____ 1. Past tense endings /t/, /d/, /id/
____ 2. Word stress

Reading: Hotel de la Ville
____ Focus on vocabulary
____ Focus on comprehension

Review Quiz	Score
Listening comprehension	____ / 8
Listening for language	____ / 10
Grammar 1	____ / 9
Grammar 2	____ / 4
Grammar 3	____ / 5
Vocabulary	____ / 5
Pronunciation	____ / 3
Reading	____ / 8
Objective 1: Ask and talk about past events	____ %
Objective 2: Talk and read about travel	____ %

C.2 A Better Place

As you complete each section of the CD-ROM course, make a check (✓). Write your scores for the Review Quiz.

Listening
____ Focus on comprehension
____ Focus on language

Speaking
____ The landlady's role
____ Kate's role

Grammar
____ 1. Comparative adjectives
____ 2. Similarities and differences: As . . . as
____ 3. Comparing nouns

Vocabulary
____ Renting an apartment (Your time ____:____)

Listening Challenge
____ Extended listening
____ More listening: Rentals

Pronunciation
____ 1. Noun, adverb, and adjective stress
____ 2. The sound /s/ and s-blends

Reading: Housing Advertisements
____ Focus on vocabulary
____ Focus on comprehension

Review Quiz	Score
Listening comprehension	____ / 9
Listening for language	____ / 9
Grammar 1	____ / 13
Grammar 2	____ / 3
Grammar 3	____ / 2
Vocabulary	____ / 5
Pronunciation	____ / 3
Reading	____ / 8
Objective 1: Describe people, places, and things	____ %
Objective 2: Compare two people, places, or things	____ %

Name _____ Date _____

C.3 Somewhere Around Here

As you complete each section of the CD-ROM course, make a check (✔). Write your scores for the Review Quiz.

Listening
_____ Focus on comprehension
_____ Focus on language

Speaking
_____ Kate's role
_____ Luis's role

Grammar
_____ 1. Superlatives
_____ 2. Definite and indefinite articles and no article
_____ 3. Review of pronouns, possessive nouns, and possessive adjectives

Vocabulary
_____ Outdoor places (Your time _____:_____)

Listening Challenge
_____ Extended listening
_____ More listening: Bus tour

Pronunciation
_____ 1. Stress for understanding
_____ 2. Plural noun endings

Reading: Beautiful Portofino
_____ Focus on vocabulary
_____ Focus on comprehension

Review Quiz	Score
Listening comprehension	_____ / 9
Listening for language	_____ / 8
Grammar 1	_____ / 8
Grammar 2	_____ / 4
Grammar 3	_____ / 6
Vocabulary	_____ / 5
Pronunciation	_____ / 3
Reading	_____ / 8
Objective 1: Describe places	_____ %
Objective 2: Compare places	_____ %
Objective 3: Read about places	_____ %

C.4 It's Spicy!

As you complete each section of the CD-ROM course, make a check (✔). Write your scores for the Review Quiz.

Listening
_____ Focus on comprehension
_____ Focus on language

Speaking
_____ Sam's role
_____ Emi's role

Grammar
_____ 1. Review of questions
_____ 2. Relative pronouns and relative clauses
_____ 3. Tag questions

Vocabulary
_____ Tourism (Your time _____:_____)

Listening Challenge
_____ Extended listening
_____ More listening: Recipe

Pronunciation
_____ 1. Stress in noun compounds
_____ 2. Stress in sentences with *that* and *who*

Reading: A Cultural Festival
_____ Focus on vocabulary
_____ Focus on comprehension

Review Quiz	Score
Listening comprehension	_____ / 9
Listening for language	_____ / 9
Grammar 1	_____ / 6
Grammar 2	_____ / 5
Grammar 3	_____ / 7
Vocabulary	_____ / 5
Pronunciation	_____ / 3
Reading	_____ / 8
Objective 1: Ask about cultural items	_____ %
Objective 2: Explain cultural items	_____ %
Objective 3: Read about customs	_____ %

⊙ PROGRESS CHECKS

C.5 You Gotta Do It!

As you complete each section of the CD-ROM course, make a check (✓). Write your scores for the Review Quiz.

Listening
_____ Focus on comprehension
_____ Focus on language

Speaking
_____ Ana's role
_____ Chris's role

Grammar
_____ **1.** Present perfect
_____ **2.** Present perfect and past tense
_____ **3.** Review of verb tenses

Vocabulary
_____ Career changes (Your time _____ : _____)

Listening Challenge
_____ Extended listening
_____ More listening: Job offer

Pronunciation
_____ **1.** Shortened phrases: *Gotta* and *oughta*
_____ **2.** Shortened phrases: *Havya* and *arya*

Reading: Job Search
_____ Focus on vocabulary
_____ Focus on comprehension

Review Quiz	Score
Listening comprehension	_____ / 8
Listening for language	_____ / 10
Grammar 1	_____ / 5
Grammar 2	_____ / 7
Grammar 3	_____ / 6
Vocabulary	_____ / 5
Pronunciation	_____ / 3
Reading	_____ / 8
Objective 1: Talk about news	_____ %
Objective 2: Ask and talk about experiences	_____ %
Objective 3: Read materials related to job interviews	_____ %

A.1 | Do I Know You?

Listening

🎧 **A. Listen to Track 1.** *Chris is talking to Sam, the taxi driver.*
Check (✓) the phrases you hear.

1. _____ 899 Union Street
   __✓__ 989 Union Street
2. _____ the man from the travel office
   _____ the guy from the travel office
3. _____ You went to our office last week.
   _____ You came into our office last week.
4. _____ You look familiar, too.
   _____ You look good, too.
5. _____ I work there part-time.
   _____ I work there full-time.
6. _____ Two jobs. Sounds busy.
   _____ Two jobs. Sounds crazy.
7. _____ How's your trip?
   _____ How was your trip?
8. _____ Do you travel often?
   _____ Do you travel a lot?
9. _____ I have to travel for work.
   _____ I like to travel for work.
10. _____ I'm in management.
    _____ I'm in sales.

🎧 **B. Listen to Track 2.** *Ana is calling Gray Taxi. Answer the questions. Circle the correct answer.*

1. Where is Ana now?   404 Battery Street / 440 Battery Street
2. Where is she going?   600 Bay Street / 606 Bay Street
3. When will the taxi come?   in 5 to 10 minutes / in 10 to 20 minutes
4. Where will Ana wait for the taxi?   inside the building / in front of the building

Vocabulary

Label the pictures. Use the words in the box.

cashier	designer	instructor	intern
office worker	waiter	musician	small business owner
taxi driver	travel agent	programmer	sales representative (sales rep)

1. _____waiter_____

2. _____

3. _____

4. _____

5. _____

6. _____

7. _____

8. _____

9. _____

10. _____

11. _____

12. _____

Grammar 1

Study Tip
Try it out!
Use new grammar points in your speech and writing. Don't be afraid to make mistakes.

Statements and *Yes/No* Questions with *Be**

Complete the conversations. Use the words in the box.
You may use some words more than once. Capitalize as necessary.

a	an	are	he's	I'm	is	she's	they're	we're	you

1. Emi: This is Maria. _____She's a_____ student in my English class.

   Laura: Nice to meet you, Maria.

2. Ana: I'd like to introduce you to Chris and Clara. _____ sales reps here at Silica.

   Gilberto: Glad to meet both of you.

3. Julie: Excuse me. _____ Ana Pedroso?

   Ana: Yes, that's right.

   Julie: Hi, _____ Julie Burns. _____ assistant manager in the sales department.

4. Luke: Excuse me. _____ from Globe Technologies?

   Luis: Yes, that's right.

   Luke: Hello, I'm from Alcova. My name _____ Luke Watson.

5. Ana: Hello, this is Janet Philips, and I'm Ana Pedroso. _____ designers at Silica.

   Luis: It's nice to meet you both.

6. Jin: Is that Mr. Brown?

   Emi: Yes, that's right. _____ instructor in the English program.

---

*To review the grammar points, see the Grammar Explanations at the end of each unit.

The Simple Present Tense: Statements and *Yes/No* Questions

Read the information about Chris, Ana, Kate, Sam, and Luis. Then complete the questions and responses. Use long responses.

Chris Redmond

Ana Pedroso

Kate Taylor

Sam Weiss

Luis Mendez

	Works	**Speaks**
Chris	Silica Communications	English, some Spanish
Ana	Silica Communications	English, Spanish, Portuguese
Kate	I-Travel	English, French
Sam	I-Travel / Gray Taxi Company	English only
Luis	Globe Technologies	English, Spanish, some French

1. **A:** _Does Kate speak_____ 2 languages?

    B: Yes, she speaks English and French.

2. **A:** Does Ana speak Spanish?

    B: _Yes, she speaks Spanish_____. She also speaks Portuguese and English.

3. **A:** _____?

    B: Yes, they work at I-Travel.

4. **A:** _____ at Globe Technologies?

    B: No, she works at Silica Communications.

5. **A:** Does Luis speak Spanish?

    B: _____. It's his native language.

6. **A:** _____?

    B: No, he works at Silica Communications.

7. **A:** _____?

    B: Kate speaks a little French, but Sam doesn't speak any French.

8. **A:** _____?

    B: Yes, he works at Gray Taxi. He also works at I-Travel. He has two part-time jobs.

Grammar 3

Short Answers to *Yes/No* Questions

Read the conversations in Grammar 1 on page 3 again. Then read the questions and write short answers, such as **Yes, she is** *or* **No, she doesn't**. *If there is no information, write* **No Information**.

1. Are Maria and Laura good friends? _____

2. Do Chris and Clara work for Silica? _____

3. Are Chris and Clara sales reps? _____

4. Is Julie Burns the manager of the sales department? _____

5. Does Luke Watson work for Globe Technologies? _____

6. Do Luke and Luis work at the same place? _____

7. Are Ana and Janet designers? _____

8. Do Ana and Janet work at the same place? _____

9. Is Mr. Brown a teacher in the English program? _____

Application Activities

1. **Vocabulary.** Make vocabulary cards for jobs and professions. Draw a small picture or symbol on 1 side of the card and write the word on the other side. Review your cards twice a week.

2. **Writing.** Write 5 sentences about yourself. Tell about your job, your hobby, your personality, your family, your living situation.

3. **Speaking and Writing.** Interview someone. Ask about his or her job, family, and hobbies. Then write 5 sentences about the person.

4. **Project.** Go to an English pen pal site on the Internet. Register and find an Internet key pal. Introduce yourself. Exchange messages.

Grammar Explanations

This section contains the same grammar explanations that are found on the CD-ROM. They are included here for your quick reference. To view the animated presentation, go to the Grammar section of Unit A.1 in the CD-ROM course.

Grammar 1: Statements and *Yes/No* Questions with *Be*

1. We introduce ourselves with *I'm* and a name.
    Chris: Hi, I'm **Chris.**
    Sam: Hello, I'm **Sam.**

2. We often give more information about ourselves.
    Sam: Hello. I'm Sam. **I'm an assistant at I-Travel.**
    Chris: Hi, I'm Chris. **I'm in sales at Silica Communications.**

3. We can also use a *yes/no* question to start an introduction.
    Sam: Excuse me. **Are you Chris Redmond?**
    Chris: Yes, that's right.
    Sam: Hi, I'm Sam Weiss.
    OR
    Sam: **Are you from Silica Communications?**
    Chris: Yeah, that's right. I'm Chris Redmond. You're from I-Travel.
    Sam: Right. I'm Sam Weiss.

4. Here's how we introduce other people:
    Chris: Bill, this is Clara Fisher. She's in sales, too.
    Bill: Nice to meet you, Clara.
    Clara: Nice to meet you, too.

Contractions of the Verb *Be*

Singular		Plural	
I am	I'm	we are	we're
you are	you're	you are	you're
he is	he's	they are	they're
she is	she's		
it is	it's		
Sam is	Sam's		

5. We make statements with the present tense of *be* like this:
    I'm a teacher.
    He's a waiter.
    We're students.
    They**'re** in sales at Silica.

Remember, we use the word *a* with singular nouns that begin with consonant sounds. Here are the consonants: B, C, D, F, G, H, J, K, L, M, N, P, Q, R, S, T, V, W, X, Y, Z.
    a waiter
    a teacher

We use the word *an* with singular nouns that begin with vowel sounds.

Here are the vowels:
A, E, I, O, U.
    an assistant
    an employee

6. We use the word *not* to make the negative form.
    Sam's a taxi driver. Sam's **not** a teacher.
    They're salesmen. They're **not** waiters.

7. We contract negative statements with *is not* and *are not* in 2 ways.
    He is not busy. →
        He **isn't** busy. / He**'s not** busy.
    They are not busy. →
        They **aren't** busy. / They**'re not** busy.

Negative Contractions of the Verb *Be*

Singular	Plural
I'm not	we're not = we aren't
you're not = you aren't	you're not = you aren't
he's not = he isn't	they're not = they aren't
she's not = she isn't	
it's not = it isn't	
Sam's not = Sam isn't	

8. To make questions with the verb *be*, we change the order.
    Sam is a taxi driver.
    Is Sam a taxi driver?
    They are students.
    Are they students?

Grammar 2: The Simple Present Tense: Statements and *Yes/No* Questions

1. We use the simple present tense for facts and things that happen again and again.
    Chris **takes** a trip every month.
    Sam **gets up** at 5:00 a.m. every day.
    Chris **speaks** 2 languages.
    Sam **works** for I-Travel.

2. We use the simple present tense with *like, love, need, have,* and *want.*
    Chris **likes** his job.
    I **love** grammar.
    We **want** your job!

3. Use the simple form of the verb with *I, you, we, they,* and plural nouns.
    I **work** in a school.

Sam and Kate **work** at I-Travel.
The interns **work** on Monday and Wednesday.

Remember, nouns are the names of people, places, and things.

4. One form is different. We add *-s* or *-es* to the simple form of the verb with *he, she, it,* and singular nouns.
   Kate **likes** her job, too.
   Sam **reads** the Sunday *Times.*
   He **goes** to L.A.
   She **does** a lot of work.

When we use *he, she,* or *it,* the verb is spelled in 3 different ways:

- When the simple form ends in *sh, ch, x, s, z,* or *o,* we add *-es.*
   I teach.
   Emily teach**es.**

- When the simple form ends in a consonant plus *y,* we change the *y* to *i* and add *-es.*
   We study.
   She stud**ies.**

- When the simple form ends in any other letter, add *-s.*
   They work.
   Sam work**s.**

   This form of the verb is called the third-person singular.

5. The verb *have* is special. We use *have* with *I, you, we,* and *they.* We use *has* with *he, she,* and *it.*
   I **have** a lot of work.
   Sam **has** 2 jobs.

6. To make the negative form of the simple present tense, we use *does not* or *do not* and the simple form of the verb. We also use the contractions *doesn't* and *don't.* For *I, we, you, they,* and plural nouns, use *do not* or *don't* and the simple form of the verb.
   I work at I-Travel.
   I **do not** work at Silica Communications.
   I **don't** work at Silica Communications.

   She lives with Sara.
   She **does not** live with Kate.
   She **doesn't** live with Kate.

7. To make a question in the simple present tense, we use *do* or *does* and the simple form of the verb. Notice the order of the words:
   They work at Silica Communications. →
      Do they **work** at Silica Communications?
   Sam works at I-Travel. →
      Does Sam **work** at I-Travel?

8. We can answer a question with a long answer.
   Dave: Does Sam work at I-Travel?
   Kate: Yes, he works at I-Travel. He's my assistant.

But usually we use short answers, especially in conversations.
   Dave: Do Chris and Clara work at Silica Communications?
   Kate: Yes, they do.
   Dave: Does Sam work there, too?
   Kate: No, he doesn't.

Grammar 3: Short Answers to *Yes/No* Questions

1. We can answer *yes/no* questions by saying only *Yes* or *No.*
   Emily: Are you at home today?
   Student: Yes.

   Paul: Is he a computer programmer?
   Laura: No.

   Laura: Do you want to go to school?
   Frankie: No.

   Laura: Does Sam drive a taxi on weekends?
   Chris: Yes.

2. For questions with the simple present of *be,* we can also answer like this:
   Paul: Are you hungry?
   Frankie: Yes, **I am.** / No, **I'm not.**

   Chris: Is I-Travel on Union Street?
   Sam: Yes, **it is.** / No, **it isn't.** / No, **it's not.**

   Emily: Are you at home today?
   Students: No, **we aren't.** / No, **we're not.**

Remember, we don't use contractions for short answers with *yes.* We don't say, ~~Yes, it's.~~

3. To answer questions in the simple present tense, we can use *do* or *does,* or *don't* or *doesn't.*
   Laura: Does Sam drive a taxi on weekends?
   Chris: Yes, **he does.**

   Chris: Do they work at I-Travel, too?
   Sam: Yes, **they do.**

   Chris: Do they work at Silica Communications?
   Sam: No, **they don't.**

Remember, we don't answer, ~~Yes, they work~~ or ~~No, they no work.~~

4. After the answer, we can add extra information.
   Laura: Are you hungry?
   Paul: Yes, I am. **That soup smells delicious.**

   Sam: Do you like your work?
   Chris: Yes, I do. **I like sales a lot.**

A.2 Somebody New

🎧 **A. Listen to Track 3.** *Laura is introducing Susan to Luis. Find 10 differences in the script below. Circle the differences. Write the correction. The first one is done for you.*

Laura: Hi.

Luis: Hi.

Laura: Are you busy?

Luis: No, what's up?

Laura: I'd like you to meet someone. Luis, this is Susan Wu. She's our new project *director* ⟨manager⟩ for the Star One program. She's from Hong Kong.

Luis: The new project director? Glad to meet you.

Susan: Nice to meet you, too.

Laura: Luis is very creative. He's an interesting guy to work with.

Luis: Thanks, Laura.

Laura: Susan has a lot of experience with the company. I'm sure you'll enjoy working with her.

Luis: Yes, I'm looking forward to working for you.

Susan: Same here, Luis.

Luis: Which room will you be in?

Laura: She'll be in the office across the hall.

Luis: The main office?

Laura: Right.

Luis: Oh. Oh, OK. When will you be moving in?

Susan: Next Monday.

Luis: So soon? Good! Well, please let me know if you need anything.

Susan: I appreciate that. Thanks.

Laura: Well, sorry for the interruption.

Luis: That's OK. See you later.

BONUS
How does Luis feel at the end of the conversation? _____

8

B. Listen to Track 4. *Luis is talking to Kate about his job. Answer the questions.*

1. How does Luis feel? _____

2. What is Kate's advice? _____

Vocabulary

Complete the crossword puzzle. Use the words in the box and the clues below.

cute	enthusiastic	friendly	funny	nervous	organized
punctual	responsible	serious	smart	talented	

Across

2. Likes to laugh and tell jokes
6. Always puts things in the correct place
9. Always on time
11. Lively and full of energy

Down

1. Quiet and thoughtful; doesn't laugh very much
3. Often stressed out
4. Intelligent
5. Takes care of everything very well
7. Has a lot of ability
8. Easy to get along with
10. Pretty; attractive

Grammar 1

Study Tip
Review the Grammar Explanations. Highlight 2 or 3 explanations. Ask your teacher to give more examples.

Adjectives

A. *Underline the adjectives in each sentence. Circle the qualifiers (for example, **really, kind of, very**).*

1. My father isn't <u>old</u>. He's (very) young. He's only 38.

2. My room is kind of small. It's not very big. I have a very tiny window.

3. The weather isn't nice today. It's terrible. It's so rainy and cold.

4. Some people say my boss, Ms. Santos, is really mean. That's not true. She's very friendly.

5. This coffee isn't very hot. It's too cold. Can I have another one?

B. *Now write about yourself. Write 3 true negative sentences (with* not*) and 3 true positive sentences. Use the words and phrases in the box.*

Adjectives		Qualifiers	Nouns
beautiful	pretty	really	I
ugly		kind of	My (friends / classmates)
great	awful	sort of	My (car / office / room / house)
new	old	a little	My (friend / neighbor / boss / teacher)
happy	sad	very	My (brother / sister / father / mother)
busy			My (husband / wife / boyfriend / girlfriend)
smart			The weather today
warm	hot	cold	
tall	short		

EXAMPLE: My friend Eriko isn't tall. She's really short.

1. _____

2. _____

3. _____

Statements with *Be* and *Have*

Complete the sentences in the chart below. Choose the correct information and use a form of **be** *or* **have**.

Age: around 40 years old, about 28 years old, 25 years old, 16 years old

Hair: long, straight, curly, black, brown, blond, light, dark

Country/Nationality: from China/Chinese, from Brazil/Brazilian, from the United States/American

Occupations: programmer at AllSoft, reporter at Veritas News Agency, students at Washington High School

Su-Lin ____is about 28____
_____years old_____.
  age

She _____
        hair
_____.

She _____
    country/nationality
_____.

She _____
        occupation
_____.

Darius _____
          age
_____.

He _____
        hair
_____.

He _____
    country/nationality
_____.

He _____
      occupation
_____.

Sarah and Andrea _____
                     age
_____.

They _____
      country/nationality
_____.

They _____
        occupation
_____.

Grammar 3

Information Questions

Complete the conversations. Use the questions in the box. Remember to include a question mark (?).

What do you want?	What's that?	Who wants it?	What kind is it?
When does he need it?	Who's that?	What time is it?	Where is she?

1. **Jin:** _Who's that?_

   Emi: That's our English teacher, Mr. Brown. I'll introduce you. Excuse me, Mr. Brown . . .

2. **Jin:** _____

   Emi: It's *rakkyo*. It's a kind of pickle. Here, try one.

3. **Luis:** I've got to give this to Laura. _____

   Susan: She's in the conference room, I think.

4. **Luis:** _____ Did the meeting start yet?

   Susan: It's about 2:55. The meeting starts in 5 minutes.

5. **Ana:** Chris, are you going to get lunch? Can you get something for me?

   Chris: Sure. I'm going to Pizza Kitchen. _____

   Ana: I'd like a calzone. A small one. Thanks.

6. **Chris:** I've got an extra doughnut. _____

   Luis: Not me, thanks.

   Paul: I'll take it. Thanks, Chris. Mmm, chocolate twist, my favorite . . .

Application Activities

1. **Vocabulary.** Make vocabulary webs. Start with 2 webs. Write these words in the middle of each web: *appearance, personality*. Draw lines to connect words. Add words like *beautiful, responsible, funny, strong*. Try to add new words each week to your vocabulary webs.

2. **Writing.** Write about your best friend. Describe your friend's personality. Write 5 sentences. Use at least 5 adjectives. Also use *very, really, a little, kind of*.

3. **Speaking.** Talk to someone about their friends and family. Ask questions like these: (to ask about appearance) *What does he/she look like?* (to ask about personality) *What is he/she like?*

4. **Project.** Find a magazine article about a famous person or search on the Internet. Write a paragraph (50–100 words) about this person or give a 2-minute presentation.

Grammar Explanations

This section contains the same grammar explanations that are found on the CD-ROM. They are included here for your quick reference. To view the animated presentation, go to the Grammar section of Unit A.2 in the CD-ROM course.

Grammar 1: Adjectives

1. Adjectives describe someone or something.
   Luis is **talented**.
   He's **great**.
   The office is **big**.

2. Adjectives come after the verb *be* to describe the subject of the sentence.
   Susan is **new** here.
   She's **happy**.

   Don't use an article (*a, an,* or *the*) with the adjective alone.
   He's nice.

3. Adjectives also come before the nouns they describe.
   Luis is great.
   Luis is **a great guy**.

   Star One is new.
   Star One is **a new program**.

   Remember, we use an article with an adjective and a singular noun.

4. Adjectives have only one form.
   They are sad, not ~~They are sads~~.

5. We can add words like *very, really, a little,* and *kind of* before adjectives.
   Very and *really* make the adjectives stronger.
   Sam is **very** nice.
   He is a **really** nice guy.

   A little and *kind of* make the adjectives weaker.
   I'm **a little** busy right now.
   He's **kind of** tired.

6. We also use adjectives called possessive adjectives. Possessive adjectives come before the noun, like other adjectives. Possessive adjectives show that something belongs to someone.
   Sam has a taxi.
   This is **his** taxi.

Pronouns and Possessive Adjectives	
I—my	I'm a taxi driver. **My** taxi is old.
you—your	Luis, **you** need a new computer. **Your** computer is really slow.
he—his	**He** has a small office. **His** office isn't very nice.
she—her	**She** has a big office. **Her** office is really beautiful.
it—its	Look at that dog. **It** has beautiful eyes. **Its** eyes are black.
we—our	**We** are teachers. **Our** students are from all over the world.
you—your	Frankie and Maggie, **you** need some clean clothes. **Your** clothes are on the bed.
they—their	**They** are students. **Their** class meets on Monday and Wednesday.

Grammar 2: Statements with *Be* and *Have*

1. Remember, we use the verb *be* to talk about occupations.
   I'm **a teacher**.
   Susan **is a project director**.
   Sam **is a taxi driver**.

2. We also use the verb *be* to talk about nationalities.
   Luis **is American**.
   He's **not Mexican**, but his family is from Mexico.
   Emi **is Japanese**.

3. We use the verb *be* to talk about age.
   Susan **is 25 years old**.
   Luis **is 24**.

4. We use the verb *be* to talk about height.
   She's **5 feet 6 inches tall**.
   She's **1.65 meters tall**.

5. We use the verb *be* to talk about feelings.
   Luis **isn't sad**.
   He's **angry**.

6. We use *be* to talk about looks.
   She's **pretty**.
   That dog **is ugly**.

7. We use *be* to talk about skills.
   Luis **is talented**.
   Susan **is smart**.
   Luis **is athletic**.

8. We use the verb *have* to describe how a person looks.
Emily **has brown eyes**.
Emily **has brown hair**.
Susan and Laura **have beautiful smiles**.

9. We use the verb *have* to show possession.
Susan **has a big office**.
Laura and Luis **have good computers**.

10. Remember, to make the negative form of *have*, use *don't* and *doesn't*. Use *doesn't* with *he, she, it*, and singular nouns. Use *don't* with the other forms.
Laura has a nice office.
Luis **doesn't have** a nice office.

Laura and Susan have big offices.
Luis and Clara **don't have** big offices.

11. Remember, to ask a question with *have*, use *do* or *does*, and the simple form of the verb.
Emi: Her office has a window.

Emi: **Does** her office **have** a window?
Luis: Yes, it has a huge window!

Grammar 3: Information Questions

1. Let's look at some information questions with the verb *be*. We begin the question with *who* to ask about a person.
Rachell: **Who's** that?
Luis: That's Susan Wu. She's the new project director.

We use *what* to ask about a thing. To ask for more information, we use *what kind* or *what type*.

Rachell: **What's** that?
Luis: It's Susan's new laptop.
Rachell: It's beautiful! **What kind** is it?
Luis: I don't know, but it's very fast.

2. We use *where* to ask about a place.
Rachell: **Where's** her office?
Luis: This is her office.

We use *when* or *what time* to ask about time.
Rachell: **When's** your first meeting with her?
Luis: This afternoon.
Rachell: **What time?**
Luis: At 3 o'clock.

3. To form information questions for most verbs, we begin with a question word, followed by *do* or *does*, followed by the subject and the simple form of the verb. Look at how we form an information question.

Susan reports to Laura.
Who does Susan report to?

Luis: **Who does** Susan **report** to?
Laura: She **reports** to me. I'm her boss.

Susan: **Where do** you **live?**
Luis: I **live** on Taylor Street, near Union Square.

Luis: **What does** Susan **want?**
Laura: She **wants** the Star One files.

Luis: **When does** she **need** my report?
Laura: She **needs** it tomorrow. I **need** it tomorrow, too.

Luis: **What time** do you **need** it?
Laura: The end of the day is fine.

4. We don't use *do* or *does* when we use *who* or *what* to ask a question about the subject.
Luis wants a really big office.
Who wants a really big office?

Remember, we don't say, ~~Who does want a really big office?~~
The Star One program costs a lot.
What costs a lot?

Remember, we don't say, ~~What does cost a lot?~~

5. We always use the third-person singular form of the verb when we use *who* or *what* to ask a question about the subject.
Emily: Who wants a big office?
Students: Luis does.
Emily: Who wants a really big office?
Student: Susan and Laura do.

A.3 | A Quick Lunch

🎧 **A. Listen to Track 5.** *Emi is ordering lunch at the Rock Café. Check (✓) the phrases that you hear.*

1. _____ the tuna fish sandwich
   _✓_ a tuna fish sandwich

2. _____ what kind of bread
   _____ what kind of a bread

3. _____ slice of tomato
   _____ a slice of tomato

4. _____ no tomato
   _____ no tomatoes

5. _____ mustard or mayo
   _____ the mustard or the mayo

6. _____ one tuna fish sandwich
   _____ some tuna fish sandwiches

7. _____ an iced tea
   _____ some iced tea

8. _____ large, medium, or small
   _____ supersize or large

9. _____ regular or decaf
   _____ regular or with milk

10. _____ with sugar or sweetener
    _____ with some sugar or some sweetener

11. _____ Why are there so many choices?
    _____ Why are there so many things?

🎧 **B. Listen to Track 6.** *A customer is calling the Rock Café with a take-out order. Write down the correct order.*

Rock Café

15

Vocabulary

Complete the conversations. Use the words and phrases in the box.

choose	meals	menu	order	snack	take-out food

1. **Chris:** What do you usually eat for breakfast?

   Ana: Actually, I usually don't eat breakfast. I eat just 2 _____ a day— lunch and dinner.

2. **Sam:** I'm going to the Rock for a _____. Do you want something?

   Kate: Oh, sure. Please bring me a diet cola and a bag of chips.

3. **Dave:** Would you like to see the _____?

   Customer 1: Oh, thank you. Let's see. I'll have a tuna fish sandwich.

4. **Dave:** Can I take your _____?

   Customer 2: Yes, please. I'd like a grilled fish sandwich and a Greek salad.

5. **Dave:** Would you like whole wheat bread, rye bread, or white bread?

   Emi: Oh, gosh. I can't decide. Please _____ for me.

6. **Susan:** I didn't bring lunch with me to work today. Does the Rock have _____?

   Luis: Oh, sure. You can order anything. I'll get it for you.

BONUS

Here are some measuring words. Can you think of one item of food for each measuring word?

EXAMPLE: a bag of _chips (cookies, peanuts)_

a can of _____   a loaf of _____

a carton of _____   a bottle of _____

a few _____   a slice of _____

a glass of _____   a stick of _____

a jar of _____   a cup of _____

Grammar 1

Count and Non-Count Nouns

A. *Complete the sentences. Circle* **a**, **an**, *or* ∅ *(no article).*

1. **Luis:** Excuse me, Susan. Can you help me? I need **a / an /**(**∅**) advice.

   Susan: I'm sorry. I can't help you now. I don't have **a / an / ∅** time.

2. **Ana:** What happened in the hallway? There's **a / an / ∅** water all over the floor.

   Clara: I spilled **a / an / ∅** glass of water. Don't worry. I'll clean it up.

3. **Maggie:** It's **a / an / ∅** bad weather today. Do you still want to walk to the station?

   Emi: Sure. Let's go. I'll get **a / an / ∅** umbrella.

4. **Chris:** Excuse me. I need **a / an / ∅** information about Flight 201.

   Agent: Flight 201 is departing in 30 minutes. Do you need **a / an / ∅** ticket?

5. **Customs agent:** Excuse me, sir. What's in this suitcase?

   Chris: I just have **a / an / ∅** clothing in that suitcase. I have several shirts and **a / an / ∅** jacket.

6. **Kate:** It's Julia's birthday. Let's have **a / an / ∅** fun tonight.

   Ana: OK. I've got **a / an / ∅** idea. Let's go out somewhere. I'll make **a / an / ∅** reservations for us at Lasaro's.

B. *Put each noun in the box into the correct category. Is it usually a count or a non-count noun?*

advice	apple	baggage	bread	chair	cheese	dollar
education	English	experience	fun	idea	jar	knowledge
love	meat	milk	money	music	oil	pepper
salt	sandwich	ticket	time	weather	woman	work

Count	Non-count
chair	knowledge

Quantifiers: *Some* and *Any*

*A. Write sentences. Use **some** and **any**.*

1. have / two brothers, no sisters

    I have two brothers, but I don't have any sisters.

2. want / coffee, tea

_____

3. need / a new notebook, pens

_____

4. will buy / juice, soda

_____

5. know / French, Spanish

_____

6. there are / Brazilian students, Japanese students / in my class

_____

7. there is / butter, milk / in my refrigerator

_____

*B. Write short answers to the questions. Use **some** or **any**.*

1. Do you have any money with you right now?

_____

2. Do you want some tea?

_____

3. Are there any good students in your class?

_____

4. Do you have any good rock CDs in your CD collection?

_____

Grammar 3

Quantifiers: *How Much, How Many, a Little, a Few*

Write sentences. Use the words in parentheses. There is one extra word in each group.

1. Hurry up. (much / don't / we / many / time / have)

   <u>We don't have much time.</u>

2. Would you like something to drink? (glass / yes, / I'd / a / some / iced tea / of / love)

   _____.

3. Let's buy a ticket for the Lala concert now. (only / there / a few / some / are / left)

   _____.

4. Would you like some milk in your tea? (little / just / few / a)

   _____.

5. Gee, Luis, your company is really big. (much / how / do / many / you / employees / have)

   _____?

Application Activities

Study Tip
Don't forget! Use the CD-ROM Progress Checks on pages xiii–xx. Add notes: new words and expressions.

1. Vocabulary. How many "abstract" nouns do you know (for example, *experience, love, education*)? Make a list of at least 20 abstract nouns. Are they count or non-count nouns? Use each one in a sentence.

2. Vocabulary and Grammar. Go to a grocery store, look at a photo of a grocery store, or visit a grocery store website. Make a list of at least 50 grocery items you can buy. Use measuring words (like "a bottle of") if necessary.

3. Writing. Make a list of things you'd like to buy at a grocery store. Include some of these words: *box, bottle, can, carton, five, large, small, dozen, loaf, kilo, pound, ounce, jar, piece.*

4. Speaking. Talk with someone about food. Ask: *What are your favorite foods? What do you usually eat for breakfast? For lunch? For dinner? What do you like to cook?*

5. Project. Go to a restaurant review website or find a review in a newspaper or magazine. Then write a short review of a restaurant. What foods does it serve? What do customers think of the restaurant?

Grammar Explanations

This section contains the same grammar explanations that are found on the CD-ROM. They are included here for your quick reference. To view the animated presentation, go to the Grammar section of Unit A.3 in the CD-ROM course.

Grammar 1: Count and Non-Count Nouns

1. Words like *sandwich, hamburger,* and *apple* are count nouns. We can count these items. We use *a, an,* or *one* with singular count nouns. We use *a* before a word that begins with a consonant sound and *an* before a word that begins with a vowel sound.
   a sandwich
   one hamburger
   an apple

2. Count nouns can be plural. To make a regular count noun plural, we add *-s* or *-es.*

a sandwich	sandwich**es**
one hamburger	hamburger**s**
an apple	apple**s**

   Some count nouns have irregular plurals. We don't add *-s* or *-es.* Here are some irregular count nouns:

a man	men
a woman	women
a child	children
a person	people

3. We use a count noun with singular and plural verbs like this:
   Dave: The sandwich **is** good.
   Rich: The sandwiches **are** awful.

4. Words like *time* and *help* are non-count nouns. We can't count time and help. Non-count nouns don't have plural forms. Non-count nouns don't use *a* or *an.*
   Luis needs **help** with his project.
   He doesn't have **time** to finish everything.

   Here are some common non-count nouns:

bread	fun	salt
cheese	information	sugar
clothing	milk	tea
coffee	pepper	water
fruit	rice	work

5. When we want to measure non-count nouns, we use words like *kilos* and *pounds.* We can also use these words to measure count nouns.
   a kilo of rice (non-count)
   2 kilos of beans (count)
   a pound of coffee (non-count)
   5 pounds of cookies (count)
   a jar of mustard (non-count)
   1 jar of pickles (count)
   a carton of milk (non-count)
   a carton of eggs (count)
   a loaf of bread (non-count)
   a piece of lettuce (non-count)

6. When a non-count noun is the subject of a sentence, the verb is always singular.
   Customer: Dave, **this milk is** bad!
   Dave: Sorry.
   Customer: And **this coffee tastes** funny, too.
   Dave: Here's another cup.

7. We use *how many* to ask about count nouns. We use *how much* to ask about non-count nouns.
   Emi: **How many sandwiches** do you make every day?
   Dave: Oh, about 100, maybe more.
   Emi: Dave, **how much bread** do you order every day?
   Dave: Emi, we order about 10 loaves of bread.

8. We can use *the* before singular count nouns, plural count nouns, and non-count nouns.
   Emi: **The sandwich** is good. (count)
   Dave: **The tomatoes** are great. (count)
   Emi: **The bread** is good, too. (non-count)

9. To make a general statement, do not use an article before plural count nouns and non-count nouns.
   Tuna sandwiches are good.
   French bread is good.

Grammar 2: Quantifiers: *Some* and *Any*

1. We use *some* and *any* with plural count nouns and non-count nouns. We use these words to talk about general amounts or quantities.
   Frankie: I'd like **some chips**, but I don't want **any tomatoes**. (count)
   Paul: I'd like **some coffee**, but I don't want **any milk**. (non-count)

2. We use *some* in affirmative sentences.
   Emi: I'd like **some** iced tea.
   Dave: Rich, I need **some** iced tea and **some** lemons.
   Rich: OK, just a second.

3. We use *any* in negative statements.
   Emi: I don't want **any** mustard, and I don't want **any** chips, either.
   Dave: OK.

4. We can use *some* or *any* in questions.
   Dave: Do you want **any** desert?
   Emi: No, I don't. Just a sandwich is fine.
   Dave: Do you want **some** pickles?
   Emi: Yes, I do. I love pickles.

5. We sometimes use *some* or *any* in a short answer. We don't repeat the nouns.

> **Dave:** Do you have **any money**?
> **Rich:** **No**, I don't have **any**.
> OR
> **Rich:** No, I don't.

> **Dave:** Do you have **any money**?
> **Rich:** **Yes**, I have **some**.
> OR
> **Rich:** Yes, I do.

Grammar 3: Quantifiers: *How Much, How Many, a Little, a Few*

1. It's easy to count words like *sandwiches, hamburgers,* and *apples.* These are count nouns. We can use *a, an,* or *one* before singular count nouns. We can use numbers before plural count nouns.

> **a** sandwich
> **an** apple
> **3** hamburgers

2. When we don't know the number of things we are talking about, we can use *many, a lot of, some,* or *a few* with count nouns. These words are called quantifiers.

> We have **a lot of oranges**.
> We have **some bananas**.
> We don't have **many apples**.
> We have **a few melons**.

3. Remember, to ask about quantity with count nouns, we use *how many*.

> **Dave:** **How many** sandwiches do you want?
> **Emi:** Just one.

4. We can use measure words with words for containers to count both non-count and count nouns. Here are some examples:

> **a bowl** of soup (non-count)
> **2 bowls** of soup (non-count)

> **a cup** of coffee (non-count)
> **3 cups** of coffee (non-count)
> **a jar** of mustard (non-count)
> **2 jars** of mustard (non-count)
> **a slice** of bread (non-count)
> **2 slices** of cake (non-count)
> **a piece** of fruit (non-count)
> **2 pieces** of bread (non-count)
> **a glass** of milk (non-count)
> **2 glasses** of water (non-count)
> **a pound** of apples (count)
> **a carton** of eggs (count)
> **a can** of beans (count)

5. When we don't know the number of things we are talking about, we can use *a lot of, some, a little,* or *not much.*

> We have **a lot of** coffee.
> We have **some** coffee.
> We have **a little** coffee.
> We **don't** have **much** coffee.

6. Remember, we use *how much* to talk about non-count nouns.

> **Dave:** **How much** sugar do you want in your tea?
> **Emi:** Just a little.

7. We can answer with *a lot* for both count and non-count nouns. We use *a few* for count nouns and *a little* for non-count nouns.

> We have **a lot of** milk.
> We have **a lot of** potato chips.

> We have only **a few** tomatoes.
> We have only **a little** rice.

A.4 What a Weekend!

🎧 **A. Listen to Track 7.** *Ana is telling Chris about her weekend. Complete the summary. Choose the correct word or phrase and write it in the blank.*

Ana had an _____interesting_____ weekend. She was
_{1. boring / interesting}

in _____ on Saturday and Sunday.
_{2. Los Angeles / San Francisco}

She did a lot of _____ activities, like
_{3. tourist / expensive}

shopping and going to movie studios. She had a

_____ time, but she said that she
_{4. great / terrible}

spent _____ money. She went with
_{5. too much / not enough}

_____. They _____ because they
_{6. some friends / some relatives}   _{7. flew / drove}

got a cheap airline fare. Ana _____ at someone's
_{8. stayed / visited}

house, not at a hotel. She _____
_{9. invited / told}

Chris to go with them on their next trip.

🎧 **B. Listen to Track 8.** *Chris is calling U.S. Rail for information. Answer the questions.*

1. Where is Chris planning to go?

   From _____ to _____.

2. How much is the fare?

   One way: _____ Round-trip: _____

Vocabulary

Study Tip
Try to memorize 2 or 3 specific phrases from the CD-ROM video. Use these phrases when you speak in English.

A. *Unscramble the letters to make travel words. Then match the words and definitions.*

<u>d</u> **1.** oursitt   <u>tourist</u>

_____ **2.** serreve   _____

_____ **3.** inechck   _____

_____ **4.** usedchle   _____

_____ **5.** erfa   _____

_____ **6.** lecnac   _____

a. The price you pay for a plane or train ticket

b. Ask for a place on a plane, in a hotel, in a restaurant, and so on

c. Go to the desk at an airport and register

d. A person who travels just for fun

e. Decide not to keep an appointment

f. A time plan for a week, a month, and so on

B. *Complete the sentences. Use the words in Exercise A.*

1. What's your <u>schedule</u> next week? Do you have any free time?

2. The _____ from London to New York is only $299. It's really cheap!

3. Can you _____ an inexpensive hotel room for us in New York? We will need it for 4 nights.

4. I'm afraid I have to _____ my plans to go to Mexico during spring break. I don't have any money to buy the ticket!

5. Do we have to _____ at the airline counter? Or can we go directly to the gate?

6. I don't have any business plans in Japan. I'm just going to be a _____ and see all the famous places.

The Past Tense of *Be*: *Was* and *Were*

Today is October 10th. Laura and Paul Arnello were busy yesterday. Look at their schedules. Then look at each sentence. If the sentence is true, write **Yes, he was / she was / they were***. Correct the sentences that are not true.*

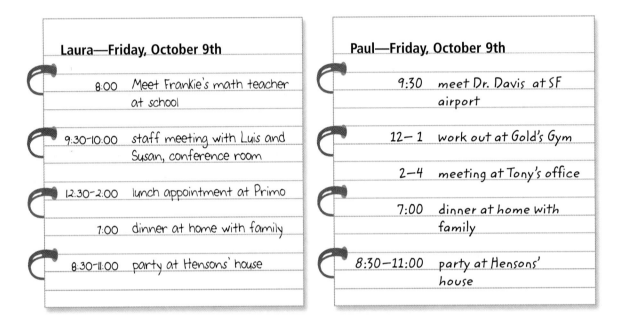

Laura—Friday, October 9th

8:00	Meet Frankie's math teacher at school
9:30–10:00	staff meeting with Luis and Susan, conference room
12:30–2:00	lunch appointment at Primo
7:00	dinner at home with family
8:30–11:00	party at Hensons' house

Paul—Friday, October 9th

9:30	meet Dr. Davis at SF airport
12–1	work out at Gold's Gym
2–4	meeting at Tony's office
7:00	dinner at home with family
8:30–11:00	party at Hensons' house

1. Laura was at home on Friday at 8 a.m.

    No, she wasn't. She was at Frankie's school.

2. Laura was at a restaurant on Friday at 1:00.

    _____

3. Paul was at the airport Friday morning.

    _____

4. Paul was at Tony's office at 3:00.

    _____

5. Paul and Laura were at a party on Friday night.

    _____

6. Laura and Paul were in their offices on Friday at 7 p.m.

    _____

7. Paul was at the gym during his lunch hour.

    _____

8. Paul was at his office all day on Friday.

_____

9. Laura was at Frankie's school on Friday afternoon.

_____

10. Paul and Laura were both at Primo for lunch on Friday.

_____

BONUS
Write 3 questions about Paul's or Laura's schedule.

EXAMPLE: __Where was Paul at 7 p.m.? Was Laura at home at 8 a.m.?_____

1. _____
2. _____
3. _____

Grammar 2

The Simple Past Tense: Regular Verbs

Complete the conversations. Use the correct form of the verb in parentheses.

1. **Kate:** What _____*did you do*_____ (**do**) last night?

   Luis: Not much. I just _____ (**stay**) at home and _____ (**watch**) television.

2. **Laura:** Where _____ (**be**) you this morning? You _____ (**not be**) at the meeting.

   Luis: There _____ (**be**) a meeting this morning? Oh, no! I forgot all about it!

3. **Kate:** Sam, it's 9:30. What happened?

   Sam: I'm sorry, Kate. I just _____ (**arrive**) a few minutes ago. I _____ (**miss**) the bus.

4. **Ana:** How _____ (**be**) your holiday in Hawaii?

   Kate: Super. It _____ (**be**) warm and sunny. I _____ (**love**) it.

   Ana: Where _____ (**stay**)?

   Kate: I _____ (**stay**) at a really nice hotel in Waikiki.

The Simple Past Tense: Irregular Verbs

A. Complete the conversations. Use the correct form of the verb in parentheses.

1. **Paul:** Did you enjoy the movie, honey?

   Maggie: Not really, Dad. I ____thought____ (**think**) it was stupid.

2. **Frankie:** Look, Mom! I _____ (**find**) a mouse in the garden.

   Laura: Keep that outside. Don't bring it in the house.

3. **Ana:** So, Kate, you have a new boyfriend?

   Kate: Um-hmm. His name is Andre. I _____ (**meet**) him at the
   24 Club last weekend.

4. **Kate:** Where did Susan work before she started at your company?

   Luis: I think she _____ (**come**) from Alta Systems.

B. Write the past tense form of each verb—5 of them are regular (end in -ed) and 9 of them are irregular (don't end in -ed).

1. borrow ____borrowed____   8. get _____

2. break _____   9. give _____

3. catch _____   10. go _____

4. change _____   11. meet _____

5. come _____   12. practice _____

6. enjoy _____   13. see _____

7. find _____   14. want _____

C. Choose 5 of the verbs in Exercise B. Write true sentences about yourself.

1. _____ last night.

2. Yesterday _____.

3. _____ in my last English class.

4. _____ last Saturday.

5. When I was a child, _____.

Application Activities

1. **Grammar.** Get a newspaper. Read it for 15 minutes. Underline all the past tense verbs you can find. Then make a list of the verbs in two groups: regular past tense and irregular past tense.

2. **Writing.** Write about a holiday. Write at least 5 sentences. Answer these questions in your writing: *Where did you go? What did you see? What did you do? How much money did you spend? Would you like to go back again?*

3 **Speaking.** Ask a couple of people questions about their weekend activities. Ask questions like *What did you do last weekend? Where did you go? What was the highlight (best part)?*

4. **Project.** Choose a famous place, like Los Angeles, London, or Tokyo. Go to a website about that place or find a brochure. Make a list of at least 7 tourist activities for the place you chose. Give a presentation to the class. Compare all student presentations. Which place has the best tourist activities?

Grammar Explanations

This section contains the same grammar explanations that are found on the CD-ROM. They are included here for your quick reference. To view the animated presentation, go to the Grammar section of Unit A.4 in the CD-ROM course.

Grammar 1: The Past Tense of *Be*: *Was* and *Were*

1. *Was* and *were* are the past tense of *be*. Use *was* with *I, he, she, it*, and singular nouns.
   I **was** at home all weekend.
   He **was** in L.A. on Saturday and Sunday.

2. Use *were* with *you, we, they*, and plural nouns.
   We **were** at the movies on Sunday.
   They **were** at the beach.

Past Tense of *Be*	
Singular	**Plural**
I was	we were
you were	you were
he, she, it was	they were

3. To make *yes/no* questions, we change the word order.
   You were in L.A. this weekend.
   Were you in L.A. this weekend?

   Kate was with you.
   Was Kate with you?

4. To make information questions, we add question words like *who, what, where, when*, and *how* before *was* and *were*.
   Ana: **How** was your weekend?
   Chris: Boring. **Where** were you?
   Ana: In L.A.
   Chris: **Who** was with you?
   Ana: Emi and Sam.

   Remember, there are 2 ways to form questions with *who*.
   Chris: Who were you with?
   Emi: I was with Ana.

   Chris: Who was with you?
   Emi: Ana was with me.

5. In the negative, we use *was not* and *were not* or the contractions *wasn't* and *weren't*. We usually use contractions in conversations.
   Chris was at home all weekend.
   Ana was not at home all weekend./Ana wasn't at home all weekend.

   Laura and Paul were at the movies on Saturday.
   Emi and Sam were not at the movies on Saturday./ Emi and Sam weren't at the movies on Saturday.

6. To answer *yes/no* questions, we use *was* and *were* in the long answer and the short answer.
   Dave: Ana, **were** you here last week?
   Ana: No, I **wasn't**.

   Dave: Ana, **were** you here last week?
   Ana: No, I **was** away on vacation.
   Dave: **Were** Chris and Luis with you?
   Ana: No, they **weren't**. They **were** in the city all week.

7. To talk about the past, we can use adverbs. Here are some examples:
   I was here **yesterday**.
   Last week Sam was here.
   Laura and Paul weren't here on **Saturday**.
   Last weekend Chris wasn't here.
   Emi wasn't here **last year**.

   Note: Adverb expressions can come at the beginning or end of the sentence.

Grammar 2: The Simple Past Tense: Regular Verbs

1. We use the simple past tense to talk about actions or events in the past.
   I stay at home on weekends.
   I **stayed** at home last week.

   I study Spanish.
   I **studied** Spanish.

2. There is only 1 form of the simple past tense. Simple past tense verbs end in *-ed*.
   work   work**ed**
   arrive   arriv**ed**
   study   stud**ied**

The Simple Past Tense	
Singular	**Plural**
I worked	we worked
you worked	you worked
he, she, it worked	they worked

3. To make negative statements, use *did not* or *didn't* and the simple form of the verb.
   Chris **did not** go to L.A./Chris **didn't** go to L.A.
   We **did not** stay home./We **didn't** stay home.

4. To make *yes/no* questions, use *did* and the simple form of the verb. Notice the order of the words.
   I stayed home all weekend.
   Did you stay home all weekend?

   Ana: **Did** you **stay** home all weekend?
   Chris: Yes, all weekend!
   Ana: **Did** you **work** all weekend?
   Chris: I work**ed** on Saturday.

5. We can answer a *yes/no* question with a long answer or a short answer.

Chris: Did you stay in a hotel?
Ana: No, we **didn't**. / No, we **stayed** with Sam's brother.

Chris: Did Emi and Sam stay with you?
Ana: Yes, they **did**. / Yes, we all **stayed** with Sam's brother.

6. To make information questions, add question words.
   Chris: I watched TV on Saturday night.
   Ana: **What** did you watch?

7. Here are other information questions:
   Who did you talk to?
   What did he want?
   Where did they stay?
   When did you arrive?

8. Remember, there are 2 ways to make information questions with *who* and *what*.
   Laura: **Who talked** to you?
   Luis: The sales manager talked to me.
   Laura: **Who did you talk to** after that?
   Luis: I talked to one of the sales assistants.
   Paul: **What started** the problem?
   Laura: I'm not sure. I think Maggie is mad at Frankie.
   Chris: I watched TV on Saturday night.
   Ana: **What did you watch?**

9. To talk about a time in the past, we can use expressions with *ago*.
   Dave: When did you arrive in the United States?
   Emi: On May 21st, **almost a year ago**.
   Kate: When did he go to New York?
   Sam: **Two days ago.**
   Maggie: When did they leave?
   Frankie: **Just a minute ago.**

Grammar 3: The Simple Past Tense: Irregular Verbs

1. Many common verbs do not end in *-ed* in the simple past. They have irregular past tense forms.
   I see her every day.
   I **saw** her last week.
   He **saw** a great movie yesterday.

   Remember, the irregular past tense forms of *be* are *was* and *were*.

Common Verbs with Irregular Past Tense Forms		
begin—began	have—had	send—sent
come—came	know—knew	sit—sat
do—did	meet—met	tell—told
eat—ate	put—put	write—wrote
go—went		

2. With irregular verbs, we make statements in the past tense like this:
   Emily has a lot of work today.
   Emily **had** a lot of work **yesterday**.
   Emi sees Laura every night.
   Emi **saw** Luis **last night**.

3. To make negative statements, we use *did not* or *didn't* and the simple form of the verb. We form negative statements with regular and irregular verbs in the same way.
   Emily had a lot of work yesterday.
   Emily **didn't have** a lot of work last week.
   Emi saw Luis last night.
   Emi **didn't see** Kate last night.
   Ana stayed in L.A.
   She **didn't stay** in San Diego.

4. We make *yes/no* questions with irregular verbs in the same way as with regular verbs. For *yes/no* questions, we use the simple form of the verb with *did* and change the order like this:
   Maggie: Ana **wrote** 10 emails yesterday.
   Frankie: **Did** she **write** to her dad?
   Maggie: She **sent** her dad a package this morning.
   Frankie: **Did** she **send** him a birthday present?
   Emi: Maggie **told** Paul the news.
   Frankie: **Did** she **tell** him about the accident?

5. We can answer a *yes/no* question with irregular verbs with a long or a short answer, just like with regular verbs.
   Clara: **Did** you **get** those sunglasses in L.A.?
   Ana: Yes, I **did**. / Yes, I **got** them in Beverly Hills.
   Clara: **Did** you **shop** every day?
   Ana: Yes, we **did**. / Yes, we **shopped** 'til we dropped! You know me!

6. To make information questions with irregular verbs, add question words and *did*. Then change the order of the subject and verb just like with regular verbs.
   We stayed in L.A. last weekend.
   Where did you stay?
   We went to L.A.
   Where did you go?

   Here are some other information questions.
   When did you get to L.A.?
   How did you get there?

7. Remember, there are two ways to form information questions with *who* and *what*.
   Chris: **Who went** to L.A.?
   Ana: Emi, Sam, and I went to L.A.
   Chris: **Who did you go with?**
   Ana: I went with Emi and Sam.
   Chris: **What went** wrong with the flight?
   Ana: Nothing went wrong. Everything was perfect.
   Chris: **What did you go to?**
   Ana: We went to all the movie studios and a really good show.

A.5 Working Smart

🎧 **A. Listen to Track 9.** *Frankie is asking his mom for help. Match each expression in the left column with a similar expression in the right column.*

_h_	**1.**	Can you show me how to use this math program?
___	**2.**	Just type the numbers in column 1.
___	**3.**	Do I have to hit "return"?
___	**4.**	And that's the answer?
___	**5.**	You don't have to think!
___	**6.**	You have to learn how to add numbers the real way.
___	**7.**	The real way? This is the real way!
___	**8.**	That's a good question.
___	**9.**	You won't always have a computer.
___	**10.**	Why not?

a. You have to type the numbers in column 1.

b. Is that the right answer?

c. That's an important question.

d. You need to learn to add numbers in your head.

e. You can do it without thinking!

f. Sometimes you'll need to work without a computer.

g. That doesn't make sense to me!

h. How do I use this math program?

i. Do I need to hit "return"?

j. What do you mean by "the real way"?

🎧 **B. Listen to Track 10.** *A customer is calling Eversoft Help Center. Answer the questions.*

1. What's the customer's problem? _____

2. How does the customer feel at the beginning? _____

3. How does she feel at the end? _____

4. Is the customer agent calm? _____

5. Is he helpful? _____

6. Does the customer thank the agent at the end? _____

Vocabulary

Here are some instructions from the Access Software user's manual. Fill in the missing words. Use the words in the box.

browse	delete	download	freeze	insert	log on

Internet Basics

(1) **Section 1.21** Accessing your email

From the "Mail" page, you have to _____ to your email account. First you need to type in your username in the top square. Then type your password into the bottom square.

(2) **Section 1.35** Cleaning up your email files

You may not wish to save all your old email files. If you want to _____ an email, simply highlight that email and press "Control" + D.

(3) **Section 1.47** Putting pictures into an email document

You may wish to _____ a picture into an email. To do this, click on the icon of the picture file, and drag it into your email document.

(4) **Section 1.55** Opening Internet pages

If you wish to _____ the Internet, you have to type in a URL (like this: www.longman.com) or click on a link from any web page (a link looks like this: **www.longman.com**).

(5) **Section 1.63** Saving files from the Internet

If you wish to _____ a file from the Internet, click on the page you wish to save. Then select "Save" from the "File" menu. You have to type a name for the file. Then press "Return" and the file will be saved on your desktop.

(6) **Section 2.76** Troubleshooting

Sometimes your computer will _____ and you will not be able to move the cursor. In this case, you must restart your computer. You can do this by pressing the "Power" key on your keyboard.

Can, Should, and Have to

A. Look at the charts. Write two sentences about each person.

	Can	**Can't**
Chris	speak English and a little Spanish	speak French
Emi	speak English and Japanese	speak Spanish
Kate	speak English and French	speak Spanish

1. (Chris)   Chris can speak English and a little Spanish. Chris can't speak French.

2. (Emi) _____

3. (Kate) _____

	Should	**Shouldn't**
Laura	help Frankie with his homework	do Frankie's homework for him
Luis	hang out more with his friends	watch so much television
Paul	get more exercise	eat so many fatty foods

4. (Laura) Laura should help Frankie with his homework. Laura shouldn't do Frankie's homework for him.

5. (Luis) _____

6. (Paul) _____

	Has to	Doesn't have to
Sam	get up every day at 7 a.m.	work at I-Travel every day
Frankie	do some housework every day	do homework on the weekends
Maggie	do the grocery shopping for her family sometimes	cook meals for her family

7. (Sam) _Sam has to get up every day at 7 a.m. Sam doesn't have to work at I-Travel every day._

8. (Frankie) _____

9. (Maggie) _____

B. *Now make sentences about yourself or people you know. Write about language, sports, special abilities, obligations at home or school.*

1. (can) _____

2. (shouldn't) _____

3. (can't) _____

4. (don't have to) _____

5. (should) _____

6. (has to) _____

Grammar 2

Imperatives: Giving Instructions

Complete the instructions. Use the imperative form of the verbs in the box. Capitalize as necessary.

do	do	change	touch	be	raise	make	stand

Warm up

Before you swim, (1)_____*be*_____ sure to warm up.

(2)_____ your arms over your head. Then

(3)_____ circles with your arms. (4)_____

this 10 times. Then (5)_____ directions. Next,

(6)_____ your toes and (7)_____ up slowly.

(8)_____ this 5 times. Now, you're ready to swim.

Have fun!

put	place	go	sit	be	breathe	smile	don't hurry

Doing a lotus pose

To do a lotus pose, you need to be flexible. First, (9)_____ on the floor. (10)_____ sure to sit up straight. (11)_____ your left foot on your right thigh. Then (12)_____ your right foot on your left thigh. (13)_____ slowly. (14)_____.
(15)_____ deeply. (16)_____!

Grammar 3

Adverbs of Manner

Look at each underlined word. Is it an adjective or an adverb?

Ana is very <u>careful</u> when she drives. She drives very <u>carefully</u>.
     1.   2.

There's only 10 minutes before the post office closes. We'd better finish <u>quickly</u>.
   3.

I don't believe it. Mr. Arnello is always here at exactly 8:00. He's so <u>punctual</u>. He never comes <u>late</u>.
   4.   5.

I can't read this note. What does it say? Chris doesn't write <u>clearly</u>.
                                                              6.

Chris is so frustrated. He's studied Spanish for 5 years, but he still can't speak <u>fluently</u>.
      7.

Jin is <u>angry</u> today. He studied really <u>hard</u> for the test, but he still did <u>badly</u> on it.
      8.   9.   10.

Emi, I'm sorry you're <u>sick</u> today. Get <u>well</u> soon, OK?
                     11.   12.

Luis, can you come in <u>early</u> tomorrow? I need to talk with you about an <u>important</u> project.
                     13.
       14.

The volleyball coach really likes Maggie's speed. She runs so <u>fast</u>!
                                                              15.

1.   adjective
2.   adverb
3.   _____
4.   _____
5.   _____
6.   _____
7.   _____
8.   _____
9.   _____
10. _____
11. _____
12. _____
13. _____
14. _____
15. _____

BONUS

Write 3 true sentences using adverbs. Use some of the verb + adverb combinations in the box.

appeared suddenly	spoke softly	played terribly	did it carefully
tried hard	sat there calmly	fell madly in love	slept deeply
got there early			

EXAMPLE: ___Our soccer team played terribly yesterday. We lost our match 5–0.___

1. _____

2. _____

3. _____

Application Activities

Study Tip
Choose 2 Application Activities. Complete the activities this week!

1. **Vocabulary**. Think of computer terms in English. What computer terms do you know that are the same in English and in your language? Write at least 5 words or phrases. Compare your words with those of your classmates.

2. **Grammar.** Look at 1 page in a book or a news article. How many adverbs can you find? Make a list of at least 15 adverbs. How many of the adverbs end in *-ly*?

3. **Writing.** Write your "resolutions." What do you have to do? What should you do? What do you want to do? Why do you want to do these things?

4. **Project.** Find a "how-to" book or website. Find something that you can teach your classmates. Make a list of at least 5 actions. Give a short demonstration to your class. Answer their questions.

Grammar Explanations

This section contains the same grammar explanations that are found on the CD-ROM. They are included here for your quick reference. To view the animated presentation, go to the Grammar section of Unit A.5 in the CD-ROM course.

Grammar 1: *Can, Should,* and *Have To*

1. Words like *can* and *should* are called modals. We always use the simple form of the verb with modals.
   I **can** speak English and French.
   Everyone **should** speak more than one language.

   We use *can* and the simple form of the verb to describe things people are able to do.
   Emily **can** speak English and some French.

2. We use *cannot* or *can't* to describe the things people are not able to do.
   Emily **cannot** speak Japanese.
   Emily **can't** speak Japanese.

3. To make questions, we change the order like this:
   Emily **can** speak Spanish.
   Can Emily speak Spanish?

   When we begin the question with *can't*, it usually means we think the answer will be *no*.
   Student: **Can't** Emily speak Spanish?
   Student: No, but she **can speak** English and some French.

4. Use *can* or *can't* for short answers to *yes/no* questions.
   Kate: **Can** Luis speak French?
   Ana: **Yes**, he **can**. He **can** speak Spanish, too.
   Kate: **Can** he speak Japanese?
   Ana: **No**, he **can't**.

5. To make information questions, add the question word, and change the order like this:
   Luis can speak 3 languages.
   What languages can Luis speak?

   Here are other information questions:
   Who can work tonight?
   Where can we get dinner?
   When can you give me the Star One report?
   How can you finish this by tomorrow?

6. We also use *can* to make a request.
   Frankie: **Can** you show me how to use this math program now?
   Laura: Sure.
   Frankie: **Can** you show me how to use this program tomorrow night?
   Laura: Sure. We **can** do it after dinner tomorrow.
   Note: We use *can* to talk about the present or the future.

7. We use *should* to give advice or make suggestions.
   Emily: **Should** we look at some examples of modals now?
   Student: OK.
   Laura: Frankie, you **shouldn't** go out tomorrow night. You **should** do your math homework.
   Frankie: I know.
   Remember, *can* and *should* have only 1 form. They are always followed by the simple form of the verb. We don't say, *He can comes.* or *He can to come.*

8. Use *have to* to give advice or to talk about something that is necessary.
   Doctor: Emi, you **have to take** it easy for a few days.
   Emi: I know, I need some rest.
   Laura: You **have to hit** "Return" after each number.
   Frankie: Cool.

9. Use *don't* or *doesn't have to* to talk about something that is not necessary.
   Frankie: Wow. You **don't have to think**! I love it!
   Laura: Frankie, computers are great, but you **have to learn** how to add numbers in your head too.

10. To make a *yes/no* question, use *do* or *does* with the simple form of *have*. Remember, use the simple form of the verb after *have to*.
    Chris: **Does** Ana **have to work** late tonight?
    Clara: Yes, she **has to work** late every night this week.
    Chris: **Do** Emi and Jin **have to study**?
    Luis: Yes, they do. They **have to finish** an assignment for Professor Brown.

11. Use *do* or *does* for short answers.
    Frankie: **Do** I have to go to bed right now?
    Laura: Yes, **you do**. It's after 10.
    Frankie: **Does** Maggie have to take me to school tomorrow?
    Laura: Yes, **she does**. I have to go to work early.
    Remember, *can* and *should* have only 1 form. We don't use *do* or *does* with these modals. *Have to* has 2 forms: *have* and *has*. We use *do* or *does* with *have to*. Note also that we use *have to, can,* and *should* to talk about the present or the future.

Grammar 2: Imperatives: Giving Instructions

1. One way to give instructions is to use imperatives. We form the imperative with the simple form of the verb.

Laura:	**Type** the numbers in column 1.
Frankie:	OK. Do I have to hit "Return"?
Laura:	Right. OK. **Do** it carefully.

2. For the negative form, use *do not* or *don't* plus the simple form of the verb.

Chris:	**Don't turn** here. Wait until Union Street and then turn left.
Sam:	OK.
Emi:	**Don't put** any sugar in my tea.
Dave:	OK, Emi.

Note: We don't use a subject with the imperative. We don't say, ~~You~~ *don't put sugar in my tea.*

3. To give a series of instructions, we use sequencing words. Here are some sentences using sequencing words:

Maggie:	My computer doesn't work. What should I do?
Laura:	**First,** make sure the power is on. **Then,** check all the power cords. **Next,** hit the "Reset" button. **After that,** call the computer help line.

4. When we give instructions, we often ask "confirmation questions" like this:

First, enter the numbers. **Do you understand?**
Then, highlight the column. **Are you with me?**
Next, add the numbers. **Is that clear?**

5. When someone gives instructions to us, we often ask clarification questions like this:

Did you say "enter the numbers"?
What does that mean?
Is that right?

You may also ask someone to repeat their instructions by saying:

Pardon me?
I'm sorry. I don't understand.
Could you repeat that?

Grammar 3: Adverbs of Manner

1. *Quickly* is an adverb of manner. Adverbs of manner answer the question *how?* Adverbs of manner usually come after the verb.

I speak English **quickly**.
He speaks Spanish **slowly**.

2. Most adverbs of manner are formed by adding *-ly* to the adjective.

Frankie is careful.
He works **carefully**.

Luis is fluent in Spanish.
He speaks **fluently**.

Maggie is a bad speller.
She spells **badly**.

Notice that the adverb often comes at the end of the sentence.

3. The adverb form of the words *fast, hard, early,* and *late* is the same as the adjective form.

I'm not a fast runner. (adjective)
I don't run fast. (adverb)
This is hard work. (adjective)
He works hard. (adverb)
Luis is early. (adjective)
Luis always gets to work early. (adverb)
Ana is late! (adjective)
Ana usually gets to work late. (adverb)

4. *Well* is an irregular adverb. The adjective is *good*.

Luis is a **good** swimmer.
He swims **well**.

5. We can make an adverb stronger by adding *really* or *very*, like this:

Laura:	Frankie, you slept **really late**.
Frankie:	I know. I was tired!
Laura:	Emi, you speak **very well** now.
Emi:	Thank you. I don't feel nervous anymore.
Emi:	Professor Brown is easy to understand. He speaks **really clearly**.
Laura:	I'm glad you like him.

6. When the verb has an object, the object comes between the verb and the adverb, like this:

Frankie does his homework carefully.
Emi speaks English well.

B.1 | Feeling Down

Listening

🎧 **A. Track 11.** *The doctor is giving Emi a prescription. Fill in the missing phrases in the dialog. Use the correct form of the verbs in the box. Capitalize as necessary. You will use some words more than once. Then listen to Track 11 to check your answers.*

need	do	have	give	take	fill	know

Emi: What kind of medication

(1)_____*do I need*_____?

Doctor: You (2)_____ a sinus infection, so

(3)_____ you some Azithromycin.

Emi: Azithro-*what?* What's that?

Doctor: It's an antibiotic. You (4)_____ to

take it for 5 days.

Emi: What (5)_____ with this?

Doctor: That's the prescription. (6)_____ it

to the pharmacy, and they (7)_____ it for you.

Emi: Thank you.

Doctor: Oh, and I (8)_____ you're busy, but you

(9)_____ to take it easy for a few days, OK?

Emi: I know. I definitely (10)_____ some rest.

Doctor: OK. Bye-bye.

Emi: Bye.

🎧 **B. Listen to Track 12.** *Ana is calling a health clinic to make an appointment. Answer the questions.*

1. What's her problem? _____

2. What does she want to do? _____

3. Who will she see? _____

4. When? _____

Vocabulary

What are they talking about? Write one of the words from the box on each line.

fever	headache	waiting room	infection	injury	nauseous	prescription	check up

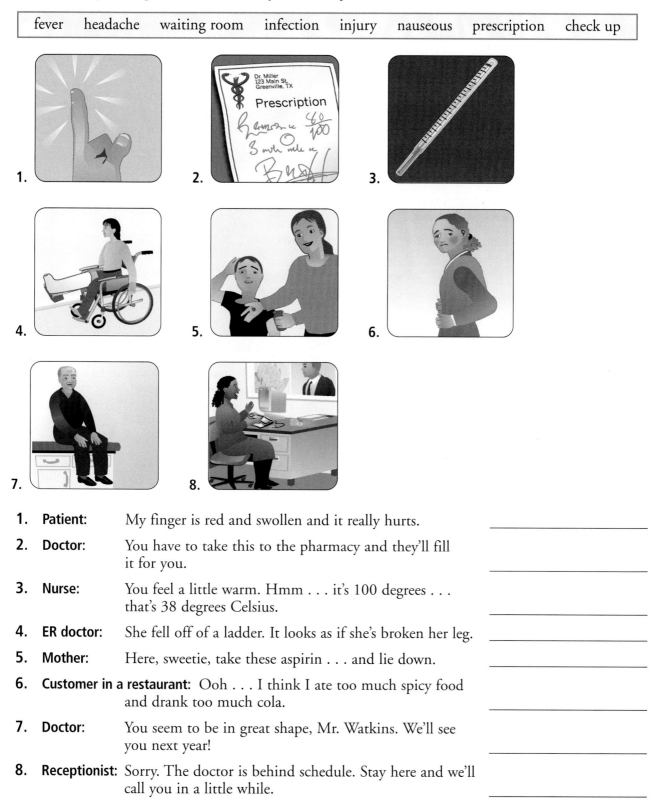

1. **Patient:** My finger is red and swollen and it really hurts. _____

2. **Doctor:** You have to take this to the pharmacy and they'll fill it for you. _____

3. **Nurse:** You feel a little warm. Hmm . . . it's 100 degrees . . . that's 38 degrees Celsius. _____

4. **ER doctor:** She fell off of a ladder. It looks as if she's broken her leg. _____

5. **Mother:** Here, sweetie, take these aspirin . . . and lie down. _____

6. **Customer in a restaurant:** Ooh . . . I think I ate too much spicy food and drank too much cola. _____

7. **Doctor:** You seem to be in great shape, Mr. Watkins. We'll see you next year! _____

8. **Receptionist:** Sorry. The doctor is behind schedule. Stay here and we'll call you in a little while. _____

What other health-related words do you know in English? Write them in the chart.

Health problems	Medications	Health professionals
stomachache	pills	nurse

Grammar 1

The Simple Present Tense and the Present Continuous

Review the rules for using the simple present or the present continuous. Then read the sentences below. For each sentence in bold, underline the verb. Which rule does the sentence use? Write the number in the blank.

Simple present	Present continuous
Rule 1: Action that happens again and again *She takes the Number 5 bus to the campus.*	Rule 3: Action that is happening right now *Frankie is doing his homework.*
Rule 2: Mental states (e.g., love, hate) *I love my English class.*	Rule 4: Actions that are changing now *It's getting warmer these days.* *What's happening with you?*

1. Don't give him any green beans. **He <u>doesn't like</u> vegetables.**   Rule __2__

2. You'd better take your umbrella. **The sky is getting dark.**   Rule ____

3. Why do you want to see *Dumb and Dumber*? **I hate that movie.**   Rule ____

4. Sorry, I can't go with you. I have to go to bed. **I get up at 5:30 every day.**   Rule ____

5. I have a lot of soft drinks in the fridge. **Do you need anything?**   Rule ____

6. I just saw Paul. He's in his office. **He's talking with Chris.**   Rule ____

BONUS
Write your own sentence for each rule.

Rule 1: _____

Rule 2: _____

Rule 3: _____

Rule 4: _____

Grammar 2

Study Tip
Listen in class. Write down other students' questions and the teacher's responses. After class, review your notes.

Stative Verbs

*Read the verbs in the box. Do you know what they mean? These verbs are often used in the stative (non-continuous) form. Complete the sentences below. Use some of the verbs in the box. Add **don't** or **doesn't** if needed. Capitalize as necessary. More than one answer may be correct.*

believe	feel like	like	need	realize	understand
belong	forget	love	own	remember	want
contain	hate	matter	prefer	suppose	wish
feel	have				

1. That new BMW ____belongs____ to Mr. Arnello. He just bought it last month.

2. I _____ her face, but I _____ her name. Is it Marla, or is it Marlene?

3. I _____ the correct answer is "C." I'm not sure, but that's my best guess.

4. I am so thirsty! I _____ a glass of water.

5. I _____ any work tonight. I _____ seeing a movie.

6. Do you want to go to the party or stay home? It doesn't _____ to me. Whatever you want.

7. Orange juice or apple juice? I _____ apple juice, if you have it.

8. _____ that today is Sunday? We don't have to get up early.

9. Decaf coffee _____ much caffeine, but there's a little in it.

10. I _____ a car, but I _____ that I had a nice one!

Asking for Clarification: Review of Questions

A. Write clarification questions. Put the words in the correct order. Capitalize as necessary.

1. "fever" / you / say / did _____?
2. call / in English / this / you / do / what _____?
3. "every other day" / mean / do / what / you / by _____?
4. say / what / you / did _____?
5. sign / does / what / mean / this _____?

B. Now match each question in Exercise A with the best response.

_____ **a.** I said, "Please get out of the way!"

_____ **b.** It means "No left turn."

_____ **c.** No, I said, "Feed her."

_____ **d.** That's a bagel.

_____ **e.** You know, like "Monday, Wednesday, Friday."

Application Activities

1. **Vocabulary.** Can you name the main parts of the body (for example, *elbow*) and the organs (for example, *lungs*) in English? Get a picture of a human body (or draw one) and label all the parts you can.

2. **Grammar.** Some verbs can be used in the continuous form (like *having*) or the simple form (like *have*), depending on the meaning. Some verbs like this are *have, see, appear, feel, think.* Use your dictionary to find out the different meanings of these verbs. Write a sentence for each verb in the continuous and simple form.

3. **Speaking.** Talk to a friend in English. Talk about 3 healthy things you do.

4. **Project.** Do you know any unusual health cures—any special diets or exercises, for example? Ask people about health practices or find some sources on the Internet. Prepare a short presentation. Make a poster. Demonstrate your ideas.

Grammar Explanations

This section contains the same grammar explanations that are found on the CD-ROM. They are included here for your quick reference. To view the animated presentation, go to the Grammar section of Unit B.1 in the CD-ROM course.

Grammar 1: The Simple Present Tense and the Present Continuous

1. Remember, we use the simple present tense for facts and things that happen again and again.
   Emi **studies** English at the university.
   She **goes** to class 3 times a week.
   Luis and Susan **work** for Globe Technologies.
   Susan **travels** to Singapore every month.

2. We use the simple present tense with *like, love, need, have,* and *want.*
   Emi **has** a fever.
   Luis and Susan **want** the corner office.
   Ana **loves** Italian food.

   Note: These verbs usually are not used in the present continuous.

3. We use the present continuous for actions that are happening now.
   It's 2 o'clock now, and Emi **is sitting** in the doctor's office.
   She and the doctor **are talking**.

4. To form the present continuous, use *am, is,* or *are,* plus the *-ing* form of the verb.
   The doctor **is examining** Emi right now.
   You **are learning** about verbs.

The Present Continuous	
Singular	**Plural**
I am talking	we are talking
you are talking	you are talking
he is talking	they are talking
she is talking	
it is talking	

   Note: If a verb ends in a silent *e*, we drop the final *e* and add *-ing: examine, examining.* If a one-syllable verb ends in a consonant, a vowel, and a consonant, we double the last consonant and then add *-ing: sit, sitting.*

   Do not double the last consonant if it is a *w, x,* or *y: play, playing.*

   Remember, you can also use contractions: *I'm talking, you're talking.*

5. To make the negative, put *not* after *am, is,* or *are.*
   Emi is eating.
   Emi is not sleeping now.
   She isn't sleeping now.

   We also say:
   She's not sleeping now.
   Luis and Susan are sleeping.
   Luis and Susan are not eating.
   They aren't eating.
   We also say:
   They're not eating.

6. To make questions in the present continuous, we change the order.
   You are waiting for the doctor.
   Are you waiting for the doctor?

   Receptionist: Are you waiting for the doctor?
   Emi: Yes, I am.

   Dr. Smith: Is Dr. Lee examining Emi Okada?
   Receptionist: Yes, she is.

   Receptionist: Are the computers working now?
   Nurse: No, they aren't.
   Receptionist: Excuse me?
   Nurse: No, they're not.

   Remember, we don't use contractions in affirmative short answers. We don't say, ~~Yes, I'm~~ or ~~Yes, she's~~.

7. To make information questions in the present continuous, put question words like *who, what, where,* and *when* before *am, is, are,* and the subject.
   Maggie is studying.
   Where is Maggie studying?

   Paul: What's Maggie doing?
   Laura: She's studying.
   Paul: Who's she studying with?
   Laura: Lisa and Brian.
   Paul: What are they studying?
   Laura: I think they have an English project.

8. *Who* and *what* can also be the subject of a question.
   Paul: Who's working now?
   Receptionist: Chris and Ana.

   Paul: What's going on in the living room?
   Laura: Frankie is playing his new CD.

Grammar 2: Stative Verbs

1. Verbs that do not describe actions are called stative verbs.
   Dr. Smith: Hi, Emi. You don't **look** good today.
   Emi: I **know**. I **feel** terrible.
   Dr. Smith: You **have** a fever.

2. Some stative verbs describe people or things.
   You **look** great.
   She's a doctor.
   It **sounds** interesting.

3. Some stative verbs describe emotions.
   Laura **loves** her children.
   She doesn't **like** dogs. She **hates** them.

4. Some stative verbs describe ideas.
   Chris **knows** Sam. He doesn't remember Sam's name.
   Chris often **forgets** names.

5. Some stative verbs describe the senses.
   This coffee **tastes** awful. I think you put salt in it, not sugar.
   The dog **smells** bad. It needs a bath.
   Emi **feels** terrible. She has a fever.

6. Some stative verbs show possession.
   This apartment **belongs** to Kate.
   She **has** a nice place.
   She **owns** some beautiful paintings.

7. Some stative verbs express needs.
   I **need** a good meal. I'm very hungry.
   Laura **wants** a cup of coffee. She's really tired.

Grammar 3: Asking for Clarification: Review of Questions

1. Clarification questions ask about meaning. Here are some examples:
   Sorry? What did you say?
   What does that mean?
   What do you mean?
   What did you say this is?
   Pardon? Did you say "fever"?

2. We can answer clarification questions with a short answer or a long answer.

Emi:	Sorry? What did you say?
Dr. Smith:	**Gesundheit!**
Emi:	What does that mean?
Dr. Smith:	**Good health.**
Emi:	How do you spell it?
Dr. Smith:	**G-E-S-U-N-D-H-E-I-T.**
Emi:	How do you pronounce it again?
Dr. Smith:	**Gesundheit.**
Emi:	What did you say this is?
Dr. Smith:	**It's a stethoscope.**
Emi:	Pardon? Did you say "fever"?
Dr. Smith:	**Yes, you have a fever.**

3. Clarification questions can ask people to repeat information.
   Pardon?
   Sorry?
   Could you repeat that?
   What did you say?
   Could you say that again, please?

   We can ask, *What?*, but this is not very polite.

4. We use *how* to ask what words mean in another language.
   Emi: **How** do you say *takusan* in English?
   Yoko: *Takusan*? We say, *a lot of*.

   Notice that information questions with *how* are formed the same way as questions with *when* and *where*.

B.2 Late Again

Listening

🎧 **A. Listen to Track 13.** *Laura and Luis are talking on the phone. Complete the dialog. Use the prepositions in the box. You will use some of the words more than once.*

| at | to | on | near | next to | about | in | with |

Laura: Luis, it's Laura. Where are you?

Luis: What do you mean—where am I? I'm here. I'm (1)_____ the office. You're talking (2)_____ me.

Laura: But we have a meeting (3)_____ Lucid Systems (4)_____ 1 o'clock!

Luis: (5)_____ 1:00? Oh, man! How do I get (6)_____ Lucid?

Laura: It's (7)_____ Ashby, 3121 Ashby, (8)_____ Telegraph Avenue. Take College Avenue (9)_____ Ashby, and turn right.

Luis: Got it.

Laura: Hurry!

Luis: I'm on my way.

Laura: Oh, Luis?

Luis: Yeah?

Laura: Be sure to bring the Lucid file.

Luis: Where is it?

Laura: I put it (10)_____ your desk this morning.

Luis: You did?

Laura: Remember? I put it (11)_____ your computer.

Luis: Oh, right. Yeah, here it is.

Laura: And Luis, please hurry. I need to talk to you about . . .

Luis: OK, we'll talk (12)_____ it when I get there. Bye.

🎧 **B. Listen to Track 14.** *You are calling to get directions to the Civic Arena. Imagine that you are in San Francisco. Complete the directions.*

Take Highway _____ to Highway _____ North. Go _____ _____ to First Street, _____ at First Street, and turn _____. The Civic Arena is at the _____ of First Street and Montgomery Street.

Vocabulary

A. *Complete the sentences. Use the words in the box. Capitalize as necessary.*

block/blocks	exit	intersection	direction	location	take a right

1. Our office is in a great _____. It's near the Pine Street Station and it's close to the park.

2. If you are driving, get on Highway 4 North. Take the Pine Street _____.

3. You don't need to take a taxi. My office is 2 _____ from the train station. You can walk.

4. If you're walking, go down Main Street. _____ at Pine Street. Our office is near the corner.

5. If you see the park, you're going in the right _____. Keep going straight.

6. If you get lost, call me. I'll meet you at the _____ of Pine Street and Main Street.

B. *Look at each expression in bold. Two words or expressions to the right have a similar meaning. One has a different meaning. Cross out (✗) the one that is different.*

1.	**an intersection**	a junction	~~a traffic light~~	a crossroads
2.	**a location**	a distance	a place	a spot
3.	**this direction**	this way	this route	this destination
4.	**one block**	a section of street	a small building	a short distance
5.	**take the first exit**	get off at the first road	get into the first car	take the first street
6.	**take a right**	turn right	do it correctly	don't go left

Grammar 1

Prepositions of Location

Study Tip
Volunteer!
Say 2 or 3 things in class every
day. Ask questions.

Answer the questions. Use full sentences. Be sure to use correct prepositions.

1. Where are you right now?

   _____

2. Is anybody next to you right now? (Use: *Yes, somebody is . . .* OR *No, nobody is . . .*)

   _____

3. What is in front of you?

   _____

4. What is on your desk right now? Describe the locations of 2 things.

   _____

5. Are you sitting between 2 things right now? What are they?

   _____

6. Are you sitting on something? What?

   _____

7. What is behind you right now?

   _____

8. Where is your school or place of work?

   _____

9. What is the most famous place in your city? Where is it?

   _____

Grammar 2

Directions and Locations

Look at the map. You are at the corner of South Street and Long Road. Read the directions below. What places on the map are being described?

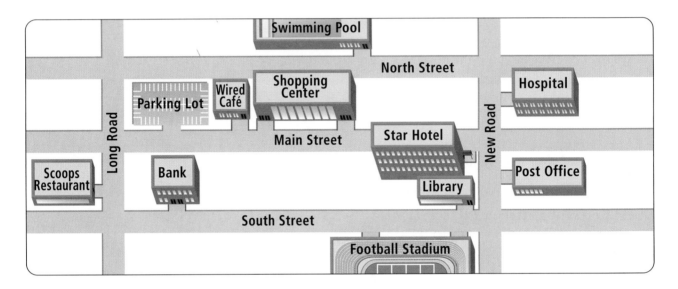

1. Take South Street to New Road. Turn left. It's on the right side of the street.

   _____

2. Take Long Road to Main Street and turn right. It's on the left side of the street. It's next to a big parking lot.

   _____

3. It's right here. It's on the corner of South Street and Long Road.

   _____

4. It's on the corner of New Road and Main Street. It's across from the post office.

   _____

5. It's between a parking lot and a shopping center.

   _____

6. It's near here. I think it's on South Street.

   _____

Grammar 3

Exclamations: Expressing Emotions

Read these short expressions that show emotions in English. (Some are from the CD-ROM course and some are new.) Then read the situations below. For each situation, give a response from the chart.

Anxiety/Worry	Relief	Surprise	Confusion	Anger	A mistake
Uh-oh . . . *Oh, no . . .*	*Whew!* *What a relief!* *Oh, that's good news.*	*Wow.* *Oh, man.* *You're kidding!*	*Oh, that's strange.* *What?!* *Huh?!*	*Darn!* *Shoot!*	*Oops.* *Oh, no.* *Uh-oh.*

Pleasure	Celebration	Displeasure	Sorrow	Pain	Disappointment
Mmm. *Cool.* *Fantastic!* *Great!*	*Hurray!* *Yay!* *Yeah!*	*Yuck.* *Arggh.*	*Oh, no.* *What a shame!* *That's too bad.* *I'm so sorry.*	*Ahhh.* *Ouch.* *Ow!* *Oof!*	*Awww.* *Oh, no.* *Aw, gee.* *What a shame.* *Oh, dear.*

1. Someone steps on your toe. _____

2. You are eating an ice-cream cone. _____

3. Your favorite football team wins the game. _____

4. You spill your drink on your shirt. _____

5. You find out that your health checkup is good. _____

6. You're waiting and waiting for the bus. It's late. _____

7. You step on some gum and it sticks to your shoe. _____

8. You find a $10 bill on the ground. _____

BONUS
Think of a new situation when you might use these expressions.

1. Cool! _____   3. Hurray! _____

2. Mmm. _____   4. What a shame! _____

Application Activities

1. **Listening and Vocabulary.** When you watch movies in English or hear English speakers, what "emotional expressions" do they use? Make a list. What do these expressions mean?

2. **Writing.** Write an email to someone. Describe how to get from that person's home to your home *or* from that person's home to your favorite meeting place.

3. **Speaking.** Talk with a classmate. Ask and answer questions about your favorite places in the city. Describe the location of each place. Possible topics are a favorite restaurant, favorite night spot, or favorite place to relax.

4. **Project.** Prepare an entertainment guide for your city. Choose at least 5 places, including at least 1 restaurant, 1 coffee shop, 1 park, 1 shop, and 1 theater. Present your entertainment guide to your class. Explain where each place is located.

Grammar Explanations

This section contains the same grammar explanations that are found on the CD-ROM. They are included here for your quick reference. To view the animated presentation, go to the Grammar section of Unit B.2 in the CD-ROM course.

Grammar 1: Prepositions of Location

1. Here are some prepositions of location:
   Next to is a preposition. It means *beside*.
       The file is **next to** the computer.
       The file is **beside** the computer.

   [file] ⟷ [computer]

2. *Between* is a preposition.
       The telephone is **between** the computer and the file.

   [computer]⟷[telephone]⟷[file]

3. *Behind* is a preposition.
       The chair is **behind** the desk.

4. *On* is a preposition.
       The file is **on** the desk.

5. *Near* is a preposition.
       The desk is **near** the door.

6. *In front of* is a preposition.
       The pen is **in front of** the telephone.

   telephone

7. *Under* is a preposition.
       The printer is **under** the desk.

   [desk]

   ↑

   [printer]

8. To give addresses, we use *on* when we give only the street name.
       Their office is **on Ashby Avenue**.

   We use *at* to talk about a place when we use the address.
       Their office is **at 3121 Ashby Avenue**.

9. With cities, states, countries, and continents we use *in*.
       Our new office is **in** New York City.
       We have 5 offices **in** New York.
       We have 3 offices **in** England and 4 **in** France.
       We also have offices **in** Asia.

10. We can use *in* or *at* with buildings like hospitals and offices. The meaning is different.
        Luis is **in** his office. (He is sitting in his office.)
        Luis is **at** his office. (He is not at home. He is working today.)
        Emi is **in** the hospital. (She is very sick.)
        Emi is **at** the hospital. (She is visiting a sick friend.)

Grammar 2: Directions and Locations

1. Here are some prepositions of direction. Read the directions and look at the map.
   Emily: How do I get to the restaurant?
   Student: Go **up** Main Street. Go **across** the Main Street Bridge. Turn right and walk **along** the river. Go **across** the Clark Street Bridge. Go **down** Clark Street. Take Maple Avenue **around** the park. It's at 12 Maple Avenue. It's called Blanca's. You can't miss it!

   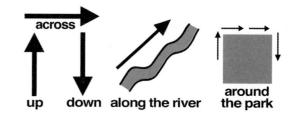

2. To give directions, we also use expressions of location. Read and look at the map.
   The bank is **on the corner**. It's **across the street** from the post office. The bank is **on the left** and the post office is **on the right**.

   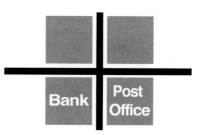

3. To give directions, we often use the imperative form of the verb. The imperative form is the simple form of the verb and never changes. Read the directions and look at the map.

Tourist: How do I get to the Museum of Modern History?

Student: We're on Ross Street right now. **Take** Ross to Bell Avenue. **Turn** right on Bell. **Go** straight on Bell. **Don't turn** left at the next street. **Turn** left at the corner of Bell and Southern. **Walk** past the Palace Theater. The museum is the third building on the right. **Turn** right. **Don't turn** left.

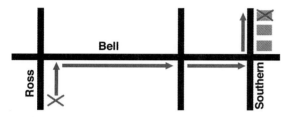

4. To ask for directions, we can use *yes/no* questions or questions with *how* or *where*.

Luis: Is Lucid far from here?

Laura: No, it isn't. You can be there in 3 minutes.

Luis: How do I get to Lucid?

Laura: Take College Avenue to Ashby and turn right.

Luis: Where's 3121 Ashby?

Laura: It's near Telegraph Avenue.

Luis: Where does the bus stop?

Laura: Don't take a bus. Take a taxi. Hurry!

5. To show how far, we use words that tell how long it takes to get somewhere.

Sam: Is the restaurant far from here?

Kate: It's about **2 miles** away.

Luis: Where's the pharmacy?

Chris: Turn left at the corner. It's about **100 feet down** on the right.

To show how far, we sometimes use words like *minutes* and *hours*.

Luis: Where's the Palace Theater?

Chris: It's near the river. It's about **10 minutes** from here.

Grammar 3: Exclamations: Expressing Emotions

1. Short exclamations are very common in conversation. Exclamations express strong emotions. Here are some exclamations of surprise:

Kate: **Gosh!** What beautiful flowers!

Sam: I'm glad you like them.

Luis: **Wow!** This coffee is hot!

Dave: Be careful!

Maggie: Guess what? I passed my math test.

Frankie: **You're kidding!**

2. Here are some exclamations we use when we are angry or when we make a mistake:

Luis: **Oh, man!** I forgot!

Laura: It's OK, but please hurry.

Paul: **Whoops!** I dropped my coffee! It's all over the carpet!

Laura: **Oh, no!** My new carpet!

3. We also use exclamations when we don't like something or when we are hurt.

Chris: **Yuck!** This tastes awful.

Emi: It's green tea. It's really good.

Ana: **Ouch!** That really hurts!

Chris: Sorry.

4. These are expressions we use when we really like something:

Emi: Do you want to try some ice cream?

Kate: Yes. **Mmm!** It's really good!

Ana: **Hurray!** It's Friday.

Chris: Fantastic.

B.3 Weekend Plans

Listening

🎧 **A. Track 15.** *Emi is giving her farewell speech. Complete the speech. Use the words in the box. Then listen to Track 15 to check your answers.*

cry	going	great	remember	special	thank	visit	will miss

I just want to (1)_____ everyone
for coming . . . this is a really (2)_____
day for me. I'm (3)_____ back to Japan
next week, but I'll always (4)_____ my
fabulous time here . . . and I (5)_____ all
of you. Someday, you'll all have to come
(6)_____ me in Japan. So thanks,
everybody, for being such (7)_____
friends. . . . I think I'm going to
(8)_____.

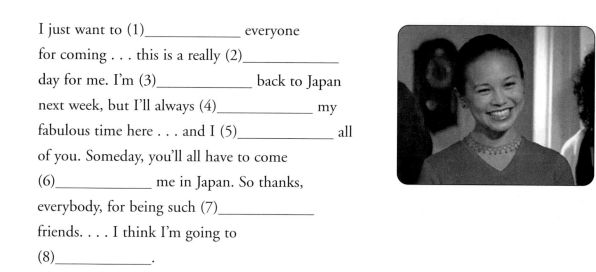

🎧 **B. Listen to Track 16.** *Somebody is leaving a message for Emi. Answer the questions.*

1. Who is it?

_____

2. Why can't he come to the party?

_____

3. What's his message?

Good _____. I hope _____.

Vocabulary

Study Tip
Choose 10 new words.
Make vocabulary cards. Review
5 cards every day.

Read about different kinds of parties. Then complete the sentences.
Use the expressions in the list.

- barbecue—a party where you cook and eat outside with friends
- New Year's Eve—on December 31st, a celebration of the coming year
- anniversary—a celebration of the day that something happened (like a wedding)
- graduation—a ceremony for someone who is finishing school
- birthday—a celebration of the day that someone was born
- costume party—a party at which special clothes are worn
- farewell party—a good-bye to someone who is leaving
- end-of-semester party—a party at the end of a school term

1. Luis had a great ___barbecue___ in his backyard last Sunday. He cooked hamburgers and hot dogs. There were about 30 people there.

2. We had a _____ party for Emi last weekend. She's going back to Japan next week.

3. There's going to be a big _____ party at my house on December 31st. You're invited—I hope you can come.

4. Ana's brother is finishing college this June. Ana is planning to host a huge _____ party for him.

5. We're having a surprise _____ party for Paul on Saturday. He's going to be 49 years old. Laura's making a big chocolate cake.

6. Let's celebrate! The semester is finally finished. Mr. Brown is hosting an _____ party at his apartment on Friday.

7. Kate invited me to a _____ party for Halloween. Everyone has to dress up. I don't know what to wear!

8. My parents are going to have their 25th wedding _____ party next month. They've been married a long, long time!

Future: *Will* and *Be Going To*

A. *Complete the sentences. Use the correct form of* **will** *or* **be going to** *and the words in parentheses. More than 1 answer may be correct.*

1. **Jin:** Where will you be tonight?

   Emi: **(probably be)** _____I'll probably be_____ at home. I have a lot of studying to do.

2. **Ana:** How will you get home after the party?

   Kate: Luis has his car. **(give me a ride)** _____.

3. **Maggie:** What are you and mom going to do tonight?

   Paul: We **(see a movie)** _____, *The Chill*. Want to come with us?

4. **Emi:** How long **(study)** _____ at the library?

   Jin: I'll probably be there until 9 o'clock or so.

5. **Chris:** **(what / do)** _____ this weekend?

   Ana: I'm going to Las Vegas with Emi.

6. **Dave:** Will you be at home tomorrow?

   Allison: I'll be home in the morning, but **(be)** _____ there in the afternoon.

7. **Clara:** **(why / go)** _____ to Miami next week?

   Chris: There's going to be a big media conference at the Convention Center.

B. *Answer the questions. Give short answers.*

1. Are you going to be at home tonight? _____

2. Will you be in English class tomorrow? _____

3. Where will you be at 9:00 tomorrow morning? _____

4. What will you do when you get home? _____

5. Are you and your friends going to see a movie this weekend? _____

Grammar 2

May and Might

A. Look at the chart.

How certain?	Modal	Example: affirmative	Example: negative
100%	will	I will go to Mexico next year.	I won't stay in the United States next year.
90–100%	going to	I'm going to go to Mexico next year.	I'm not going to stay in the United States next year.
About 50%	might	I might go to Mexico next year.	I might not stay in the United States next year.
Less than 50%	may	I may go to Mexico next year.	I may not stay in the United States next year.

B. What are your plans for tonight? This weekend? Tomorrow morning? Next month? About 5 years from now? Write sentences in the chart.

Time	*will / going to*	*might / may*
1. Tonight		
2. This weekend		
3. Tomorrow morning		
4. Next month		
5. About 5 years from now		

Grammar 3

Exclamations: Expressions for Special Occasions

Look at the pictures. Fill in the blanks. Use the words in the box. Capitalize as necessary.

anniversary	birthday	care	congratulations	happy	sorry	that's great

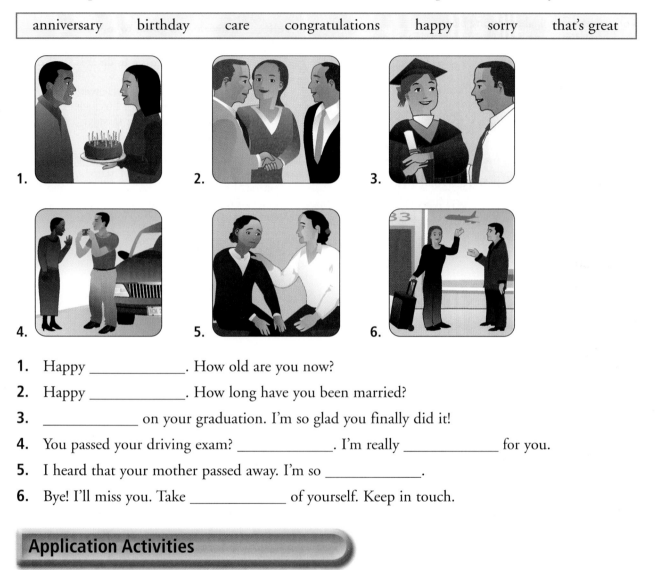

1. Happy _____. How old are you now?

2. Happy _____. How long have you been married?

3. _____ on your graduation. I'm so glad you finally did it!

4. You passed your driving exam? _____. I'm really _____ for you.

5. I heard that your mother passed away. I'm so _____.

6. Bye! I'll miss you. Take _____ of yourself. Keep in touch.

Application Activities

1. **Vocabulary**. People often celebrate holidays and other "big events." Look on the Internet to find a calendar that lists holidays and events for the United States or another country. Make a list of at least 10 holidays and the reason for the celebration.

2. **Grammar.** What will the world or your life be like in 20 years? Write 5 predictions for the future. Use expressions like these: *Probably . . . will . . ./I think that . . . might. . . .* Here are some ideas: your work, your love life, your family, money, travel, a famous person, politics.

3. **Speaking.** Talk with someone about the future. Use questions like these: *What are you going to do tonight? This weekend? During the next vacation? What will your life be like in 5 years?*

4. **Project.** Imagine that you are at a going-away party. The party is for you! Write a short speech like Emi's farewell speech. Give your farewell speech to the class.

Grammar Explanations

This section contains the same grammar explanations that are found on the CD-ROM. They are included here for your quick reference. To view the animated presentation, go to the Grammar section of Unit B.3 in the CD-ROM course.

Grammar 1: Future: *Will* and *Be Going to*

1. We use *am, is,* or *are* with *going to* and the simple form of the verb to talk about future plans.

    Chris: **I'm going to take** a present to Emi's party tonight.
    Ana: Chris, we**'re** all **going to take** presents!

Future with *Be Going to*	
Singular	**Plural**
I am going to move.	We are going to move.
I'm going to move.	We're going to move.
You are going to move.	You are going to move.
You're going to move.	You're going to move.
He is going to move.	They are going to move.
He's going to move.	They're going to move.
She is going to move.	
She's going to move.	
It is going to move.	
It's going to move.	

2. We make the negative form of *be going to* like this:

    Chris: Clara **isn't going to be** at Emi's farewell party.
    Luis: Jin and Yoko **aren't going to be** there either.

    I'm not going to move.
    You're not going to move.
    He's not going to move.
    She's not going to move.
    It's not going to move.
    We're not going to move.
    You're not going to move.
    They're not going to move.

    Remember, we can also say *you aren't, he isn't, she isn't, it isn't, we aren't,* and *they aren't.*

3. To make *yes/no* questions, we change the order like this:

    He's going to take Emi some flowers.
    Is he going to take Emi some flowers?

4. We can answer *yes/no* questions with long or short answers.

    Chris: Are you going to take Emi some flowers?
    Ana: **Yes, I am. / Yes, I'm going to buy some at the supermarket.**
    Chris: Are you going to get Emi a present?
    Yoko: **No, I'm not. / No, I'm going to get her a card.**

    Remember, the short answer uses only a form of *be.* We say, *Yes, I am.* We don't say, *Yes, I'm going to.*

5. To make information questions, put a question word before *am, is,* or *are going to* and the simple form of the verb, like this:

    Jeff: **Who are you going to meet?**
    Oscar: Marta. We're going to see a movie.

    Susana: **What are you going to do this weekend?**
    Janet: I'm going to visit Mary.
    Susana: **When are you going to leave?**
    Janet: I'm going to take the 12 o'clock express.
    Susana: **Where are you going to stay?**
    Janet: I'm going to stay with her.

6. We can also use *will* and the simple form of the verb to talk about future plans. In conversations, we usually use contractions.

    Sam: **I'll be** at Emi's around 7:00.
    Kate: Great. **I'll be** there around 8:00.

Contractions with *Will*	
I will → I'll	we will → we'll
you will → you'll	you will → you'll
he will → he'll	they will → they'll
she will → she'll	
it will → it'll	

7. When we use *will,* we can answer a *yes-no* question with a long answer or a short answer. In conversations, we usually use short answers.

    Dave: **Will** you **be** here this afternoon?
    Rich: **Yes, I will.**

    Remember, we don't use contractions in the affirmative short answer. We don't say, *Yes, I'll.*

    Dave: **Will** you **be** here tomorrow?
    Emi: **No, I won't.** I have an English test.

    Note: The negative form of *will* is *will not.* The contraction is *won't.*

8. Ask information questions with *will* like this:

    Chris: Where **will** Luis **meet** us?
    Emi: At my office.
    Chris: When **will** he **be** there?
    Emi: At 7:30.

9. Finally, we can use the present continuous to talk about the future. We show that we are talking about the future by using future time expressions like these:

    Ana: **I'm having** dinner with Emi **tomorrow night.**
    Kate: That's nice. **Where are you going?**

    Ana: **Are you going** to the party **next week?**
    Chris: Absolutely.

    Chris: Where **are you buying** Emi's present **tonight?**
    Ana: At a store in my neighborhood.

Grammar 2: *May* and *Might*

1. We usually use *going to* or *will* to talk about future plans when we are sure they are going to happen. We use *may* and *might* to talk about future plans when we are not sure they are going to happen.

Kate: What are you going to do this weekend?
Chris: I'm **going to go** to Emi's party Saturday night. I'm not sure about Sunday. I **may go** to a movie with Luis. What are you going to do?
Kate: I **might go** to the beach with Ana.

2. We use *may* or *might* with the simple form of the verb. *May* and *might* have almost the same meaning.
I **may** have dinner with my friends tomorrow.
He **might** have dinner with his friends tomorrow.

3. We form negative statements by putting *not* between *may* or *might* and the simple form of the verb.

Ana: Kate, I **may not get** all my work done by Sunday, so I can't go to the beach with you.
Kate: Oh, too bad.
Luis: I **might not go** to the movies with you tonight.
Chris: That's OK.

Note: We never contract *may*. We don't say, ~~I mayn't~~. In American English, we don't contract *might*. We don't say, ~~I mightn't~~.

4. We don't use *may* or *might* in questions about future plans. When we use *may* in a question, it means something different.

Maggie: Mom, may I go to the movies with Brian?
Laura: No, Maggie. Not tonight.

In this question, Maggie wants to go to the movies. She is asking her mother for permission to go.

Note: We don't use *might* in questions to ask for permission.

5. We can also use *may* and *might* in short answers.

Chris: Are you going to give a speech at your farewell party?
Emi: I don't know. I might, or I might not.
Chris: Don't be shy!

Grammar 3: Exclamations: Expressions for Special Occasions

1. At special times and on holidays, we use certain special expressions. For birthdays we say:
Happy birthday!

Luis: It's my birthday today.
Ana: **Happy birthday!** Have a great day.

On wedding anniversaries we say:
Happy anniversary!
Congratulations!

Karen: What are you going to do tonight?
Laura: We're going to celebrate. It's our 15th anniversary.
Karen: **Congratulations! Happy anniversary!**

2. For important events, we can say:
Congratulations!
I'm really happy for you!
That's great!

Emi: I got an A on my English test.
Paul: **Congratulations**, Emi. **That's great!**
Chris: **Congratulations** on your new job, Ana. **I'm really happy for you.**
Ana: Thanks, Chris.

3. When something very sad happens we say:
I'm really sorry.
That's terrible.

Ana: Marcello was in a car accident. He broke his arm.
Chris: Oh, Ana, I'm **really sorry**.

4. When someone dies, we say:
I'm so sorry to hear about your father.
I'm sorry to hear about your mother's death.

Ana: **I'm so sorry** to hear about your father.
Paul: Thank you, Ana.

5. When someone is going away we say:
Good-bye! See you soon.
Bye! I'll miss you.
Take care of yourself.
Keep in touch.

Chris: Bye, Ana. **We'll miss you.**
Ana: **I'll miss you** too.
Chris: **Keep in touch.**
Ana: I will. Don't worry.

B.4 Excellent Choice!

Listening

🎧 **A. Listen to Track 17.** *Paul and Frankie are coming back from the supermarket. Fill in the missing words in the dialog.*

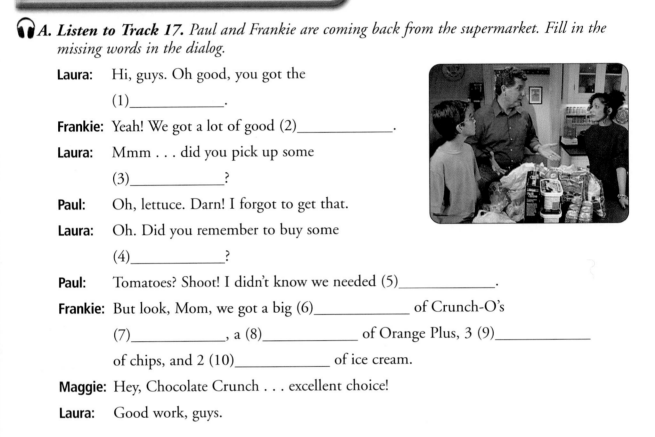

Laura: Hi, guys. Oh good, you got the

(1)_____.

Frankie: Yeah! We got a lot of good (2)_____.

Laura: Mmm . . . did you pick up some

(3)_____?

Paul: Oh, lettuce. Darn! I forgot to get that.

Laura: Oh. Did you remember to buy some

(4)_____?

Paul: Tomatoes? Shoot! I didn't know we needed (5)_____.

Frankie: But look, Mom, we got a big (6)_____ of Crunch-O's

(7)_____, a (8)_____ of Orange Plus, 3 (9)_____

of chips, and 2 (10)_____ of ice cream.

Maggie: Hey, Chocolate Crunch . . . excellent choice!

Laura: Good work, guys.

BONUS
When you go shopping for food, what do you like to buy?

_____

🎧 **B. Listen to Track 18.** *Dave is placing an order online for supplies for his café. Check (✓) the items that Dave orders.*

____ coffee   ____ French bread   ____ whole wheat bread   ____ lettuce

____ tuna fish   ____ chicken   ____ eggs   ____ onions

____ ketchup   ____ mayonnaise   ____ oranges   ____ orange juice

____ tomatoes

When will the items arrive? _____

What is the total charge? _____

Vocabulary

A. *Match the places with the definitions.*

_____ **1.** dry cleaners

_____ **2.** movie theater

_____ **3.** pharmacy

_____ **4.** coffee shop

_____ **5.** florist

_____ **6.** supermarket

_____ **7.** department store

_____ **8.** bookstore

_____ **9.** video store

_____ **10.** bank

_____ **11.** flea market

a. a place that sells flowers and plants

b. a place that sells food

c. a place that cleans clothes

d. a place that has medicines and personal items

e. a place that serves coffee and snacks

f. a place that shows movies

g. a place that sells clothes, cosmetics, and household items

h. an open market where you can buy used items

i. a place where you keep your money

j. a place that rents and sells videos and DVDs

k. a place that sells books and magazines

B. *Complete the crossword puzzle. Use the places in Exercise A.*

Across

8. You want to have your suit cleaned.

10. You'd like to look for new clothes.

11. You want to buy some flowers.

Down

1. You want to get a magazine.

2. You need to buy some toothpaste.

3. You need some used furniture.

4. You and your friend want to rent a video tonight.

5. You're going on a date and you want to see the latest movie.

6. You'd like to have a cup of coffee with your date.

7. You have to get groceries, like milk and bread.

9. You need to get some money from your bank account.

Study Tip
As you watch the CD-ROM video, list the words that are difficult to pronounce. Repeat these words every day.

Expressions with *Make* and *Do*

A. Here are some expressions used with **make** *and* **do**. *(Some are from the CD-ROM course and some are new.) Put the nouns in the correct column to make verb phrases.*

a cake	a list	math	your best
the cooking	business	an effort	some work
a decision	a mistake	your homework	the housework
the dishes	a suggestion	friends	your bed

make	*do*
a cake	business

B. Now answer the questions.

1. When we talk about work, do we use *make* or *do*? _____

2. When we talk about building or creating something, do we use *make* or *do*? _____

3. Compare these expressions: *make a cake/do the cooking* and *make your bed/do some housework*. When we don't say exactly what the activity is, do we usually use *make* or *do*? _____

Grammar 2

Expressions with *Get*

Read the list of common expressions with **get**. *(Some are from the CD-ROM course and some are new.)*
Then rewrite the sentences below using expressions with get.

receive / obtain	*become / change into*	*move / arrive*
get an answer	get tired	get out of here
get the vegetables	get cold	get to school on time
get some groceries	get _____er	get to the meeting on time
get a new car	get better	get in the car
get email	get worse	get out of the car
	get late	get on the train
		get off the train

1. I'm going to the supermarket to buy some groceries.

    _____

2. Is it 11:30 already? Wow, it's really late.

    _____

3. When will we reach the hotel? I'm really tired.

    _____

4. It's become really cold tonight. Let's turn on the heat.

    _____

5. Have you talked to Emi recently? Her English is really improving.

    _____

6. I have to see a doctor. My cold is still really bad.

    _____

7. Look, the police are coming. We'd better leave now.

    _____

8. It's 3:03. It's time to board the train.

    _____

Definite and Indefinite Articles

Fill in the blanks with **a**, **an**, **the**, *or* ∅ *(no article).*

1. **Waiter:** What can I get for you?

   Ana: I'd like ____a____ glass of iced tea, please.

2. **Ana:** What are you looking for, Chris?

   Chris: Luis's phone number. I wrote it on _____ piece of paper, but now I can't find _____ paper.

3. **Frankie:** Excuse me, do you have _____ ice cream?

   Clerk: Sure. _____ ice cream is in Aisle 5. Frozen foods.

4. **Paul:** Chris, did you finish your sales report?

   Chris: Yes, Mr. Arnello. I put _____ report on your desk this morning.

5. **Laura:** What do you guys want for dinner tonight?

   Maggie and Frankie: Let's have _____ spaghetti.

6. **Paul:** Excuse me. Where are _____ tomatoes?

   Clerk: They're in _____ vegetable section. Aisle 1.

Application Activities

1. **Vocabulary.** Make a list of at least 10 expressions that use *get, go, do, make*. Use your dictionary (you can use the Longman Dictionary in your CD-ROM course) or ask an English speaker for examples. Try to use some of these expressions when you speak and write.

2. **Reading and Writing.** In the CD-ROM Reading for this unit, you learned about the history of ice cream. Find out about another food. Write a short report telling about its history. Here are some ideas: candy bars, hamburgers, cola, popsicles, bubblegum, doughnuts.

3. **Speaking.** Talk about shopping. Ask questions like these: *Where do you shop for . . . ? What is the best place to get . . . ?*

4. **Project.** Think of 1 item in each of these categories: electronics (for example, a computer), games, furniture, sporting equipment (for example, a football), vehicles (for example, a car or a motorcycle), accessories (for example, a necklace), clothing. Write down the items. Go to an online shopping site. Write down the brand name of each item you find and the price of each item.

Grammar Explanations

This section contains the same grammar explanations that are found on the CD-ROM. They are included here for your quick reference. To view the animated presentation, go to the Grammar section of Unit B.4 in the CD-ROM course.

Grammar 1: Expressions with *Make* and *Do*

1. We use *make* and *do* in a lot of expressions. Here are some expressions with *make*:

   make a list
   Paul: I made a shopping list. Where is it?
   Frankie: It's in your shirt pocket, Dad.

   make a phone call
   Ana: Excuse me, I have to make a phone call.
   Chris: I'll wait here.

   make friends
   Emi: Ana has a lot of friends.
   Kate: Yes, she makes friends easily.

   make a mistake
   Frankie: Uh-oh, I made a mistake. I forgot the milk.
   Paul: That's OK. Go back and get some now.

   make excuses
   Frankie: I didn't finish my homework last night. I had to help my dad.
   Teacher: Frankie, don't make excuses.

   make a suggestion
   Paul: Do you want to make a suggestion?
   Ana: Yes, we need some Brazilian coffee in this office.

   make plans
   Chris: Did you make plans for the summer?
   Ana: Yes, Kate and I are going to rent a house at the beach.

2. Here are some expressions with *do*:

   do your homework
   Laura: Frankie, please do your homework.
   Frankie: I finished my math and I'm doing my English now.

   do some work
   Kate: I have to say good-bye now. I have to do some work.
   Ana: OK. I'll call you tomorrow.

   do the housework
   Emi: Did you do the housework?
   Laura: Not yet.
   Emi: Let me help you.

   do the cooking
   Laura: Paul, you always do the cooking.
   Paul: That's OK. I love to cook.

   do the grocery shopping
   Paul: Let's do the grocery shopping.
   Frankie: Sure, Dad.

Grammar 2: Expressions with *Get*

1. We use *get* in many expressions. We often use these expressions in conversations. *Get* can mean *receive*. *Receive* is more formal.
   Emi: Can you **get** email at home?
   Jin: No, I don't have a computer at home.
   Sam: I don't understand. I wrote to her three times, but I didn't **get** an answer.
   Dave: Maybe she doesn't like you anymore.

2. *Get* also means *find* or *buy*.
   Paul: I'll **get** the vegetables. You **get** the milk.
   Frankie: OK.
   Maggie: Let's get a new car next year!
   Laura: Not next year.

3. *Get* also means *to become*. It is also used with adjectives like this:
   Emi: Dave, it's **getting** late. You should go home.
   Dave: I will at 9:00.
   Laura: Why did you come home so early?
   Maggie: I **got** tired.
   Laura: Frankie, come here. Your soup is **getting** cold.
   Frankie: I'm coming.
   Laura: Don't go out without a sweater. You'll **get** sick.
   Emi: I won't, Mrs. Arnello.

4. Sometimes *get* can mean *arrive*.
   Kate: When do you **get** home in the evening?
   Dave: About 10:30.
   Chris: Excuse me. How do I **get** to the Clinton Hotel?
   Person: Go down 2 blocks and turn left.

5. There are also expressions with *get* like these:
   get in the car (enter the car)
   get out of the car (leave the car)
   get on the train (enter the train car)
   get off the train (leave the train car)

   Remember, *get* is an irregular verb. The past tense of *get* is *got*.

Grammar 3: Definite and Indefinite Articles

1. *A* and *an* are indefinite articles. We use indefinite articles when we are not talking about a specific singular count noun (a person, place, or thing).
   Paul: We need **a** shopping cart.
   Frankie: There are **a** lot of carts inside.

2. We use *a, an,* or *one* before singular count nouns.

> **Maggie:** I want **a** big box of Crunch-Os cereal.
> **Paul:**   OK, we'll get 1 box.

3. We don't use *a* or *an* with non-count nouns or plural nouns.

> **Maggie:** I want **cookies** and **milk**.
> **Paul:**   Me, too. Let's get some.

4. *The* is the definite article. We use *the* when the speaker and listener are talking about the same thing. Use *the* for specific things that the speaker and listener know about.

> **Paul:**   Let's do **the** grocery shopping.
> **Frankie:** Sure, Dad.

> **Paul:**   Did you get **the** milk?
> **Frankie:** No, I didn't.

5. We use the definite article before singular count nouns, plural count nouns, and non-count nouns.

> Here's **the shopping cart**. (count)
> **The tomatoes** are in aisle 3. (count)
> **The milk** is over there. (non-count)

Remember to use the singular form of the verb with non-count nouns.

6. We use *a* or *an* the first time we talk about a noun. We use *the* when we talk about the noun for the second time.

> **Paul:**   I made **a shopping list**. Now where is it?
> **Frankie:** **The list** is in your shirt pocket, Dad.

B.5 Sound Advice

🎧 **A. Listen to Track 19.** *Maggie is inviting Brian to a dance. Fill in the missing phrases in the dialog.*

Maggie: Hi, it's Maggie. Maggie Arnello. From third-period math.

Brian: Hey, what's up?

Maggie: Um . . . I was wondering . . . if you . . . had a date for the (1)_____ on (2)_____?

Brian: No.

Maggie: Well, I was wondering if you . . . do you want (3)_____ to the dance with me? We could just go as friends, we could . . .

Brian: You (4)_____ go to the dance with me?

Maggie: Yeah . . .

Brian: Cool. But do we (5)_____?

Maggie: Well, no . . . but it is a dance . . .

Brian: Oh . . . but I (6)_____ dress up, do I?

Maggie: No, you don't have to dress up. Well, maybe (7)_____ pick me up or something?

Brian: Sure. What time?

Maggie: Well, the dance (8)_____ at 8:00 so maybe, like, 7:30?

Brian: Yeah, cool.

Maggie: OK, great, see you later?

Brian: Later.

🎧 **B. Listen to Track 20.** *The school principal makes an announcement about the school dance. She gives 3 rules. What are the rules?*

- Rule 1: No _____ anywhere (gym, parking lot, school grounds).
- Rule 2: No _____ allowed in the gymnasium.
- Rule 3: Be out of the _____ by 11:15.

Complete the sentences from advice letters. Use the words and phrases in the box.

engaged	get along	get dressed up	have a date	propose	single

Dear Dr. Love:

1. A guy in my office invited me to go out with him. I like him (he's cute and really sweet), but we work together, so I feel a little strange. Is it OK to _____ with someone in your office?

2. I've been going out with "Louise" for about 3 years. She wants me to _____ to her, but I don't know if I'm ready. I'm worried that . . .

3. There's this great girl in my English class, "Andrea." We _____ really well. We always sit together in class and we enjoy studying together on the weekends. Recently, I've noticed that she . . .

4. I'm _____ and very happy. My problem is this: My parents are always pressuring me to get married. They keep trying to . . .

5. I need some help. "Norm" and I are _____, and we're planning to get married next month. But guess what? I'm starting to have some doubts. I'm getting cold feet . . .

6. I've got a problem with my new girlfriend, Cheryl. Problem is: She's rich and I'm just a poor student. Cheryl always wants to _____ and go out to fancy restaurants and clubs. I can't afford to spend . . .

Grammar 1

Gerunds and Infinitives

A. *Here are some common "combination verbs" in English. Which verbs are followed by gerunds (-ing form) and which verbs are followed by infinitives (to form)? Put the verbs in the correct column.*

| decide | enjoy | feel like | forget | hate | keep | learn | like | love |
| miss | need | plan | practice | prefer | promise | want | would like | |

Verb + gerund (*-ing*)	Verb + infinitive (*to*)	Verb + gerund or infinitive
enjoy	decide	hate

BONUS

Here are some new "combination verbs": **agree**, **avoid**, **expect**, **hope**, **spend time**, **stop**, **try**. Where do they belong in the chart in Exercise A?

B. *Make 2 questions and 3 statements. Combine phrases from the left column with phrases from the right column. There are several possible combinations.*

I don't enjoy	to call me last night, but he didn't
Emi doesn't feel like	to eat Mexican food tonight
Chris doesn't want	seeing her family
Does Emi miss	going to parties in the dormitory
Kate loves	speaking Spanish at work
Chris promised	to go to the dance alone
Why did you decide	to quit your job

1. _____ ?

2. _____ ?

3. _____ .

4. _____ .

5. _____ .

Giving Advice

Complete the conversations. Use the phrases in the box and the words in parentheses. More than 1 answer may be correct.

You should . . .	Maybe you could . . .
You shouldn't . . .	Why don't you . . .
Try _____ing . . .	Let's . . .
I think you should . . .	Maybe we shouldn't . . .
I don't think you should . . .	Why don't we . . .

1. **Sam:** It's raining, but I still want to go camping.

   Andy: **(not go this weekend / go next weekend)**

   _____Maybe we shouldn't go this weekend. / Why don't we go next weekend?_____

2. **Clara:** I had a fight with my boyfriend.

   Ana: **(wait for him to call you / call him and talk about it)**

   _____

3. **Kate:** Ready to go to Luis's birthday party?

   Donna: **(take a gift / take something to drink)**

   _____

4. **Maggie:** I'm really tired. I have a lot of homework to do.

   Laura: **(take a nap first / do it tomorrow morning)**

   _____

5. **Chris:** My stomach is upset.

   Tom: **(drink some green tea / not drink coffee)**

   _____

6. **Steven:** I really like Janis, but she doesn't know that I like her.

   James: **(tell her / write her a note)**

   _____

Grammar 3

Too and Enough

A. *Read the questions. Then complete the responses. Use* **too** *or* **enough**.

1. **(strong)**

   Ana: Would you like a cup of this coffee?

   Chris: No, thanks. That coffee _____

2. **(expensive)**

   Susan: Do you want to go to The Shamrock for lunch?

   Luis: No, not The Shamrock. _____

3. **(good)**

   Tommie: Why isn't Edward on the soccer team?

   Frankie: He tried out for the team, but _____.

4. **(busy)**

   Chris: Hey, Ana, Clara and I are going out for lunch. Want to come with us?

   Ana: Sorry, _____

B. *Write questions using* **too** *or* **enough**.

1. **Laura:** **(The Patio Café / too expensive)** _____ ?

   Susan: No, it's not too expensive. Let's go there for lunch.

2. **Laura:** **(this soup / hot enough)** _____ ?

   Paul: Actually, it's a little too cold. Could you heat it up for me?

Application Activities

1. **Vocabulary.** Imagine you are going on a date. Write at least 10 activities you can do on a date in your city.

2. **Reading and Writing.** Find an advice column in an English language newspaper. Find 2 problems that are interesting to you. Write your own advice.

3. **Speaking.** Talk to a classmate. Tell about a problem you have, such as with friends, with your family, with money, and so on. Ask for advice.

4. **Project.** Think about your life when you were 16 years old. What did you do? What things did you like doing? What things did you hate doing? Make notes. Give a 2-minute presentation to your class.

Grammar Explanations

This section contains the same grammar explanations that are found on the CD-ROM. They are included here for your quick reference. To view the animated presentation, go to the Grammar section of Unit B.5 in the CD-ROM course.

Grammar 1: Gerunds and Infinitives

1. Some verbs can be followed by a noun or by an infinitive. An infinitive is *to* and the simple form of the verb.

   Maggie wants **a boyfriend**. (noun)
   Maggie wants **to ask** Brian to the dance. (infinitive)

   Here are some verbs that are followed by an infinitive:

   decide
   Luis decided to leave early. He didn't like the movie.

   forget
   Chris often forgets to pay the rent. He often doesn't pay the rent.

   learn
   Kate learned to speak Italian last summer. Kate can speak Italian now.

   need
   Sam needs to call me. I have to speak to Sam.

   plan
   Sam doesn't plan to have children. Right now, Sam doesn't want to have children.

   promise
   I promise to call you tomorrow. I will call you tomorrow.

   want
   They want to leave now. They aren't happy here.

   would like
   I would like to order a salad. Please give me a salad.

2. We make questions with verbs and infinitives like this:
   Ana: Did Chris forget to pay the rent again?
   Luis: Yes, he did. He'll pay it tomorrow.

   Emi: Why do they want to leave right now?
   Kate: They're not having a good time, I guess.

3. Some verbs can be followed by a noun or a gerund. A gerund is the simple form of the verb plus *-ing*.
   Emi enjoys **books**. (noun)
   Emi enjoys **reading** books. (gerund)

   Here are some verbs that can be followed by a gerund:

   enjoy
   Ana enjoys dancing. Ana likes to dance.

   feel like
   Paul feels like cooking. Paul wants to cook something.

   keep
   The telephone keeps ringing. The telephone is ringing a lot today.

   miss
   Emi misses seeing her family. Emi would like to see her family in Japan.

4. We make questions with verbs and gerunds like this:
   Laura: Do you miss seeing your family?
   Emi: I sure do.

   Paul: Why does this phone keep ringing?
   Laura: Maggie's friends are calling.

5. Some verbs, such as *love, hate, like,* and *prefer,* can be followed by a noun, an infinitive, or a gerund.
   Kate loves **the beach**.
   Kate loves **to go** to the beach.
   Kate loves **going** to the beach.

Grammar 2: Giving Advice

1. There are many ways we ask for advice and give suggestions. We use *should* to ask for and give advice. *Should* is a modal. We use the simple form of the verb with *should*.
   Chris: What **should** I **take** to Emi's party?
   Ana: Maybe flowers or a card.

   Emily: You **should practice** your English every day.
   Student: OK.

   Should means that something is a good idea. *Should not* or *shouldn't* means that it is not a good idea.
   You **shouldn't** smoke.

2. We can make suggestions with *try* and a gerund.
   Emi: **Try calling** Brian up.
   Maggie: I can't do that. I'm too shy!

   Emily: **Try practicing** English with your friends.
   Students: We do! Sometimes.

3. Another way to make suggestions is to say, *Why don't you* or *Why don't we* plus the simple form of the verb.
   Emi: **Why don't you call** Brian up?
   Maggie: I can't!

   Students: **Why don't we study** together tonight?
   Emily: That's a great idea.

4. We also can use *how about* and a gerund.
   Ana: Chris, **how about getting** Emi a CD?
   Chris: That's a good idea.
   Kate: **How about buying** Emi some flowers?
   Chris: I don't really like flowers.

5. We can use *let's* plus the simple form of the verb to make suggestions. We can also say *let's not.*
   Kate: **Let's go** to the beach today.
   Sam: No, **let's not go** today. It's too cold!

   Remember that *let's* always includes you and me.

Grammar 3: *Too* and *Enough*

1. Remember that *very* makes an adjective or an adverb stronger.

   Emi: This cake is **very good**. Did you make it?
   Laura: No, I didn't, but I'm glad you like it.

   Laura: You did your homework **very carefully**.
   Frankie: I know. I worked hard at it.

2. Remember, *too* makes an adjective or adverb stronger. *Too* has a negative meaning. It shows that something is more than we need or want.

   Maggie: I can't call Brian. I'm **too shy**.
   Emi: Sure you can.

   Ana: I ate **too fast**. My stomach hurts.
   Emi: I'm sorry.

3. We can also use *too* with an adjective or adverb plus an infinitive to say that we *aren't going to* or *can't* do something.

   I'm **too tired to eat** dinner. I'm not going to eat dinner.

   I'm **too busy to have** breakfast. I'm not going to have breakfast.

   Maggie is **too shy to call** Brian. She's not going to call Brian.

4. *Enough* comes after an adjective or adverb. *Enough* means we have as much as we need. *Not enough* means we don't have as much as we need.

   Paul: No, you can't stay out until midnight.
   Maggie: Dad! I'm **old enough**.
   Laura: Maggie, you're only 16. You're **not old enough**.

   Frankie: Are you going to be on the swim team?
   Bill: Not this year. I'm **not fast enough**.

5. We often use *enough* with an adjective or adverb and an infinitive. This shows that something is possible.

   Maggie is **old enough to drive**. She is 16 and she can drive.

   Frankie is **good enough to be** on the swim team. Frankie is a good swimmer. He's on the swim team.

   Not enough shows that something is not possible.

   Frankie **isn't old enough to drive**. He's only 12. He can't drive.

   Bill **isn't good enough to be** on the swim team. Bill isn't on the swim team.

C.1 | Welcome Back

A. Listen to Track 21. *Kate is telling Ana about her trip. Complete the summary of Kate's trip. Use the words in the box.*

briefcase	baggage	trip	hotel	presentations	meeting
missed	wait	lost	arrived	lady	kid

Kate had a difficult (1)_____. She left her (2)_____ at 6:00 this morning, but she forgot her (3)_____ and had to go back to the hotel to get it.

Then she (4)_____ her flight, so she had to (5)_____ 2 hours for the next flight. On the plane, she sat next to a very talkative (6)_____, and a little (7)_____ was kicking her seat. (She said that she almost (8)_____ her mind!) Then, when Kate (9)_____, her suitcase wasn't at the (10)_____ claim.

She was in New York on business. She enjoyed the national (11)_____. There were lots of interesting (12)_____.

B. Listen to Track 22. *Kate is talking to an airline agent about her lost bag. What do you think the agent says? Complete the agent's questions.*

Agent: Is this _____?
Kate: Yes, this is . . .

Agent: Did you report a _____?
Kate: Yes, I reported the . . .

Agent: Were you on Flight _____?
Kate: That's right, Flight . . .

Agent: What kind of _____?
Kate: It's a . . . Luggage-Pro.

Agent: Does it have your _____?
Kate: Yes, it has my . . .

Agent: Do you need it _____?
Kate: Yes, I do need it . . .

Vocabulary

A. *Complete the sentences. Use the words in the box.*

flight attendant	documents	jet-lagged	depart	passport
baggage claim area	connection	suitcase	delayed	luggage
check . . . in	overbooked	reservation	agent	

1. Hello. I'd like to make a _____ on tomorrow's flight to Sydney, please.

2. The flight is not direct. There's a _____ in Singapore.

3. I need to ask you this, madam—did you pack your _____ yourself?

4. Could you please show me your travel _____?

5. Are you going to _____ this _____, or is it carry-on?

6. I'm sorry, sir. I'm afraid we're _____. Would you mind taking the 1 o'clock flight?

7. If you'd like to change your seat assignment, please see the _____ at the departure gate.

8. This is a long flight. I hope I don't feel _____ after we arrive.

9. Attention. Flight 981 to Singapore is _____. The new departure time is 2:30.

10. Welcome to Singapore. Please proceed directly to the _____ to retrieve your luggage.

B. *Now look at each sentence in Exercise A. Who said it—a passenger or an airline agent? Write the numbers of the sentences in the appropriate blanks.*

Airline agent: __2,_____

Passenger: __1,_____

Grammar 1

The Past Continuous

A. *Last night at 8:15, all the lights in the city went out. What were people doing when the lights went out? Complete the sentences. Use the correct form of the verbs in the box. You will not use all the verbs.*

come	cook	(not) do	drive	fly	leave	listen
paint	play	relax	study	talk	(not) watch	work

1. Emi _____ on the phone to her mother in Japan.
2. Frankie and his friend _____ a new computer game.
3. Laura _____ dinner for her family.
4. Maggie _____ for the school dance with her friends.
5. Kate and Ana _____ to music at Kate's apartment.
6. Jin _____ for a history test at the library.
7. Rich and Dave _____ the walls of the Rock Café.
8. Chris _____ anything. He _____ on the sofa.
9. Luis _____ TV (for a change!). He _____ on a report for Laura.
10. Paul _____ home from the airport. There was a big traffic jam.

BONUS
What were you doing last night at 8:15?

At 8:15 last night, _____

B. *Complete the questions. Use the correct form of the verb in parentheses.*

1. You were having fun on the computer, Frankie. What game _____? (play)
2. I saw you outside the movie theater at 9:00. Who _____ for? (wait)
3. I called you last night around 10:00, but there was no answer. What _____? (do)
4. Kate had a big suitcase when I saw her. Where _____? (go)
5. Sam was dancing with his headphones on. What music _____ to? (listen)
6. Oh, sorry, I just turned off the TV. _____ it? (watch)

Grammar 2

Study Tip
Find a study partner.
Review the grammar, vocabulary, and speaking from each unit.
Talk in English!

Review of the Past Tense

Identify the error in each conversation. Circle the letter of the error and write the correction in the blank.

1. **Dave:** Were you in New York last week, Kate?

   Kate: Yes, I <u>did</u>. I <u>was</u> at a sales meeting. I <u>had</u> a great time and <u>learned</u>
   　　　　　　(A)　　　　　(B)　　　　　　　　　　　(C)　　　　　　　　　　　(D)
   a lot.

   1. _____was_____

2. **Dave:** Was somebody <u>wait</u> for you at the airport when your flight
   　　　　　　　　　　　(A)

   <u>arrived</u>?
   　(B)

   Kate: Yes, Sam <u>was</u>. He <u>met</u> me at the baggage claim area.
   　　　　　　　　　(C)　　　(D)

   2. _____

3. **Chris:** Kate, welcome back! How <u>was</u> your trip to New York?
   　　　　　　　　　　　　　　　　　(A)

   Kate: It <u>was</u> great. I <u>meet</u> a lot of interesting people and <u>went</u> to a lot
   　　　　　　(B)　　　　　　(C)　　　　　　　　　　　　　　　(D)
   of nice restaurants.

   3. _____

4. **Karen:** Did you <u>miss</u> your flight?
   　　　　　　　　　(A)

   Kate: Yes, I <u>was missing</u> the 9 o'clock flight, so I <u>had to wait</u> 2 hours
   　　　　　　　(B)　　　　　　　　　　　　　　　　　(C)
   for the next one. I <u>was</u> so frustrated.
   　　　　　　　　　(D)

   4. _____

5. **Karen:** That was a long flight. <u>Were you able</u> to sleep?
   　　　　　　　　　　　　　　　(A)

   Kate: No, I <u>couldn't sleep</u>. There was a guy sitting next to me. He
   　　　　　　(B)

   <u>was listened</u> to the rock channel on his headphones. It <u>was</u>
   　(C)　　　　　　　　　　　　　　　　　　　　　　　　(D)
   so loud!

   5. _____

Past Tense Sequences

Laura is asking people about their day. Complete the conversations. Circle the correct word.

1. **Laura:** How was your day at school, Maggie?

   Maggie: Terrible! **First / After / Next** I had a really difficult math test.

   Then / Again / After I had to give a speech in English class. I was so nervous.

2. **Laura:** How was your day at work, Paul?

   Paul: Super! **After / First / Next** I had a terrific meeting with the people from SunSoft.

   Then / Again / After lunch, I saw an excellent presentation that Ana gave.

3. **Laura:** How was your day at school, Frankie?

   Frankie: OK, I guess, but I lost my gym shirt.

   Laura: You lost your shirt? What happened?

   Frankie: **After / When / Then** my gym class, I left my shirt in the locker room.

   When / Then / So I went back to get it, it was gone.

BONUS
Imagine that it's now 9:00 p.m. Answer Laura's question about yourself. Write at least 3 sentences.

Laura: How was your day, _____?

                          your name

You: _____

_____

_____

Application Activities

1. **Vocabulary.** Make a list of words related to travel. Divide the page into different sections: things you take with you, people and things you see at the airport or train station, and things you like to do. Try to list at least 5 words in each section. Compare your list with those of your classmates.

2. **Writing.** Describe a trip you went on. Include answers to these questions: *Who did you go with? What was the best thing about the trip?* (Describe it in detail.) *What was the worst thing about the trip?*

3. **Speaking.** Talk with someone about a trip he or she took. Ask questions like these: *Where did you go? How was the trip?*

4. **Project.** Find out about some travel "horror stories." You can search for stories on the Internet. Summarize 1 story. Present it to the class.

Grammar Explanations

This section contains the same grammar explanations that are found on the CD-ROM. They are included here for your quick reference. To view the animated presentation, go to the Grammar section of Unit C.1 in the CD-ROM course.

Grammar 1: The Past Continuous

1. To form the past continuous, we use *was* or *were* plus the *-ing* form of the verb. We use the past continuous to show an action that was continuing in the past.

   Emi: How was your flight?
   Kate: Terrible. A little boy **was kicking** my seat the whole time.

   Kate: The mother and the little boy **were talking** all the time.
   Emi: I hate that!

The Past Continuous	
Singular	**Plural**
I was kicking	we were kicking
you were kicking	you were kicking
he / she / it was kicking	they were kicking

2. To make the negative, put *not* after *was* or *were*.
   A little boy was kicking my seat.
   The little boy **wasn't sleeping**.
   He and his mother were talking.
   They **weren't watching** the movie.

   Remember, the contraction of *was not* is *wasn't*. The contraction of *were not* is *weren't*.

3. To make questions in the past continuous, we change the order. We often answer with a short answer.
   Sam was waiting for Kate at the airport.
   Was Sam **waiting** for Kate at the airport?

   Ana: Was Sam waiting for you at the airport?
   Kate: Yes, he was.
   Ana: Was your bag waiting for you?
   Kate: No, it wasn't!

4. To make information questions in the past continuous, put the question words *who*, *what*, *where*, and *when* before *was* or *were* and the subject.
   Sam was waiting for Kate.
   Where was Sam waiting for Kate?

   Chris: **What was Kate doing** in New York?
   Ana: She was at a national meeting.
   Chris: **Who was Kate helping?**
   Ana: Her brother.

5. *Who* and *what* can also be the subject of the question.
   Chris: **What** was happening in New York?
   Kate: Lots of things!

   Chris: **Who** was bothering you?
   Kate: A lady on my flight. She was talking all the time.

Grammar 2: Review of the Past Tense

1. We use the simple past tense to talk about events in the past.
   I **arrived** at the airport.
   Sam **waited** for me at the baggage claim.
   Kate **lost** her suitcase.
   Luis and Kate **were** at a party last night.

   Remember, we form the simple past tense of regular verbs by adding *-d* or *-ed* to the simple form of the verb. For irregular verbs, we don't add *-ed* in the past tense. You have to learn the irregular forms.

2. To make negative statements, we use *did not* or *didn't* and the simple form of the verb. Negative statements are formed in the same way for regular and irregular verbs.
   Kate arrived at Kennedy Airport.
   Kate **didn't arrive** at La Guardia Airport.

   She went to Manhattan.
   She **didn't go** to Boston.

3. To make *yes/no* questions, we use *did* and the simple form of the verb. *Yes/no* questions are formed in the same way for regular and irregular verbs. Notice the order of the words.
   Luis: **Did** Kate **like** her present?
   Clara: Yes, she liked it a lot.

   Chris: **Did** the airline **find** Kate's bag?
   Ana: Yes, they found it on Saturday.

4. We can answer a *yes/no* question with a long answer or a short answer.
   Chris: Did you miss your flight?
   Kate: **Yes, I missed it by about 10 minutes!**
   Chris: Did Sam meet you at the airport?
   Kate: **Yes, he did.**

5. Use the contraction *didn't* for negative short answers.
   Ana: Did you meet any cute guys at the conference?
   Kate: No, I **didn't**.
   Ana: Maybe next time.

6. To make information questions, add question words and change the order of the words like this:
   They arrived late.
   When did they **arrive**?

   They found her suitcase.
   Where did they **find** her suitcase?

   Remember, there are 2 forms of questions with *who* and *what*.
   Chris: **Who met** Kate at the airport?
   Ana: **Sam** met her at the baggage claim.

Chris: **Who did** Kate **meet** in New York?

Ana: She met **a lot of new people** from her company.

7. We often use adverbs of time with the simple past tense to show when an action or event happened.

Luis and Kate were at a party **last night**.

Ana went to Brazil **last year**.

Yesterday, Kate lost her suitcase.

A few days ago, Kate went to New York.

8. Adverbs of time can come at the beginning or at the end of a sentence.

Luis and Kate were at a party **last night**.

Last night, Luis and Kate were at a party.

Kate lost her suitcase **yesterday**.

Yesterday, Kate lost her suitcase.

Grammar 3: Past Tense Sequences

1. We can use *first* to begin a sequence of events. We use *then, next, after that*, or *finally* to talk about the things that happen next.

First, Kate forgot her briefcase and had to go back to the hotel.

Then, she missed her flight, and she had to wait for the next flight.

After that, she got on another flight.

She sat next to a lady who talked a lot.

Finally, she landed, but her bag wasn't at the baggage claim.

Note: All of the main verbs are in the simple past tense.

2. Use the past progressive with *when* and the simple past tense. This shows that 1 action stops or interrupts a second action.

Kate **was calling** the office when Sam **arrived** at the airport.

Kate **was running** through the airport when she **lost** her shoe.

Use *when* to introduce the simple past action.

Kate was calling the office **when Sam arrived** at the airport.

Kate was running through the airport **when she lost** her shoe.

This means:

First, Kate was calling the office. Then, Sam arrived at the airport.

First, Kate was running. Then, she lost her shoe.

3. We can also use the simple past with *when* to talk about a past sequence of events.

Kate: **When I forgot my briefcase**, I had to go back to the hotel.

Ana: Oh, Kate.

This means that first Kate forgot her briefcase. Then she had to go back to the hotel.

4. The part of the sentence that begins with *when* can come at the beginning or at the end of the sentence. The meaning is the same.

When I forgot my briefcase, I had to go back to the hotel.

I had to go back to the hotel **when I forgot my briefcase**.

C.2 A Better Place

Listening

🎧 **A. Listen to Track 23.** *A landlady is showing Kate an apartment. Fill in the missing words in the dialog. Use the adjectives and adverbs in the box.*

definitely	fully	quickly	lovely	long	beautiful	modern

Landlady: It has a (1)_____ view of the ocean.

Kate: That's a view of the ocean?

Landlady: And this is the garden!

Kate: This is the garden?

Landlady: And here is the kitchen . . . (2)_____
equipped with all the (3)_____
conveniences!

Kate: Ah, well, thanks for showing the place to me. I
will (4)_____ give this some consideration . . .

Landlady: Well, I would encourage you to act (5)_____. This (6)_____
place won't last (7)_____.

BONUS
Does Kate believe the landlady's descriptions? How do you know?

_____

🎧 **B. Listen to Track 24.** *Kate hears some information about apartments for rent. Fill in the chart with information about the 4 rentals.*

Address	Monthly rent	Type of property (studio apartment, 1-bedroom apartment, 2-bedroom house)	Furnished or unfurnished?	Special features (views / garden / transportation / type of neighborhood)
400 Lake St.				
2020 University Ave.				
505 Clement St.				
101 Spear St.				

Vocabulary

What do people look for in a place to live? Complete the descriptions. Use the words in the box.

| rent | convenient | view | utilities | neighborhood | furnished | spacious | lease |

1. **Tom:** I don't care much about what the apartment is like—you can make any place look like home. I just want a quiet _____—a place without much traffic.

2. **Sarah:** For me, the number 1 consideration is price. If I can't really afford the _____, I'll always be in trouble.

3. **Kelly:** I work at an office downtown and I don't drive. So the place has to be _____—close to a subway station or bus stop.

4. **Gary:** No more dark apartments for me! I've got to have a lot of light and a _____ of a park or a lake or hills or mountains. I guess I'm a nature lover at heart.

5. **Jack:** I want everything to be included in the rent—gas, electric, water. I don't want to worry each month about how much the _____ are going to cost.

6. **Gina:** I'm an actor—and I don't really stay long in one place. Sometimes I have to move out after only 3 months. My first question is always "Can I have a short-term _____?"

7. **Gabi:** I'm a student, and I don't have any furniture. I've got only a suitcase full of clothes and my laptop. So I definitely need a _____ apartment.

8. **Alan and Felicia:** We have 3 kids. Right now, we're in a small 2-bedroom apartment. It's too crowded! We've got to find a more _____ apartment.

Grammar 1

Study Tip
Talk to yourself—in English. Ask yourself *how* about things around you. For example: How big is my desk?

Comparative Adjectives

Write sentences about Luis and Chris. Use the comparative form of the adjectives given. If you can, add **much / a lot / a little**.

1. Chris is 5 feet 11 inches tall. Luis is 5 feet 10 inches tall.

   (Luis / short / Chris)

   Luis is a little shorter than Chris. _____

2. Chris works 8 hours a day, 5 days a week. Luis works 9 hours a day, 6 days a week.

   (Luis / busy / Chris)

   _____

3. Chris's rent is $1,400 a month. Luis's rent is $1,150 a month.

   (Chris's rent / expensive OR high / Luis's rent)

   _____

4. Chris's apartment is about 1,200 square feet. Luis's apartment is about 800 square feet.

   (Chris's apartment / spacious OR big / Luis's apartment)

   _____

Grammar 2

Similarities and Differences: *As . . . As*

Gilberto, Marta, Toshi and Helena are students at Big Apple Language School. Read the clues and figure out how old they are, how long they have been at Big Apple Language School, how far they live from the school, and their grades in the English class. Then complete the chart below.

Ages

Toshi is much older than the other students.
Marta isn't as old as Gilberto, but she's older than Helena.

Time at Big Apple Language School

Helena hasn't been at the school as long as the other students.
Gilberto has been at the school twice as long as Toshi.

Where they live

Toshi's home is much farther from the school than Helena's.
Helena lives closer to the school than Gilberto and Marta.
Marta lives farther from the school than Gilberto.

Grades

Toshi's English grade was worse than Gilberto's.
Helena's English grade was better than Gilberto's.
Helena's English grade wasn't as good as Marta's.

	Gilberto	**Marta**	**Toshi**	**Helena**
Ages (18, 21, 23, 31)				
Time at Big Apple Language School (2 weeks, 1 month, 2 months, 1 year)				
Distance from Big Apple Language School (½ mile, 1 mile, 3 miles, 5 miles)				
Grade on last English test (A, B, C, D)				

BONUS
Choose 4 pairs of items from the list below. Write your own opinions. Use comparative adjectives.

- Your city and another city
- American food and food from your country
- A popular singer from your country and a popular American singer
- Snowboarding and skiing
- An athlete from the United States or the United Kingdom and an athlete from your country
- Cats and dogs

1. _____

2. _____

3. (as . . . as . . .) _____

4. (not as . . . as . . .) _____

Grammar 3

Comparing Nouns

Toshi, Marta, and Gilberto are comparing New York and their hometowns. Complete the sentences. Use the words in the boxes.

a lot	more	like

Toshi: My friends in Tokyo always ask me about New York. Their first question is always "What's New York (1)___like___?" I tell them, "New York is (2)_____ like Tokyo, except that New York is even (3)_____ exciting!" Now all my friends want to visit me here!

much many	as	like	from

Marta: My American friends ask me, "Is Mexico City (4)_____ New York?" In my opinion, Mexico City is very different (5)_____ New York. First, Mexico City is (6)_____ bigger than New York. There are so (7)_____ parts to Mexico City! And the traffic in New York isn't as bad (8)_____ the traffic in Mexico City. Sometimes it can take an hour just to go a few miles.

both	than	much	similar	like

Gilberto: People ask me if Rio and New York are (9)_____. Well, in some ways, Rio is (10)_____ New York. Rio and New York are (11)_____ very exciting cities. Of course, the weather in Rio is always warmer (12)_____ the weather in New York. So people are always outside in Rio, and people aren't in such a hurry! I think the people in Rio are (13)_____ more friendly and talkative than the people in New York, too.

Application Activities

1. **Vocabulary.** Look at a list of apartment rentals in a newspaper or on a website. Look at 5 ads. Write down all the nouns you find. Look up the meaning of any unfamiliar words. Ask about any unfamiliar abbreviations (such as *lvng rm*).

2. **Writing.** Write an advertisement for your perfect home. Include details: what facilities it has, how convenient the neighborhood is, and how much the rent is.

3. **Speaking.** Talk with someone about the place where he or she lives. Ask questions like these: *What's your place like? How many rooms does it have? What do you like about it?* (Note: We usually don't ask people how much their house costs or how much their rent is.)

4. **Project.** Imagine you are going to study full time at a university in another country. Find a website that advertises housing. Find out about 3 different types of housing in one city. Compare your information with your classmates.

Grammar Explanations

This section contains the same grammar explanations that are found on the CD-ROM. They are included here for your quick reference. To view the animated presentation, go to the Grammar section of Unit C.2 in the CD-ROM course.

Grammar 1: Comparative Adjectives

1. When we have 2 people, places, or things, we can compare them. We can compare them by using comparative adjectives.

   Kate:　　This **apartment** is **bigger** than my **place**.

   Landlady: It has 2 bedrooms. A large **bedroom** . . . and a **smaller one**.

2. We make the comparative form of short adjectives by adding -er or -r.

   My car is **old**. Sam's car is **older**.

   My apartment is **nice**. Your apartment is **nicer**.

3. If the adjective ends with a vowel and a single consonant, we double the final consonant and add -er.

   Susan's office is **big**. Laura's office is **bigger**.

   It was **hot** this morning. It's **hotter** right now.

4. If the adjectives end in y, we change the y to i and add -er.

   People are **happy** on Fridays.

   People are **happier** on weekends.

   The parks are **pretty** in the winter.

   The parks are **prettier** in the spring.

5. If the adjective has 2 or more syllables, we make the comparative with more.

   Laura has a **beautiful** house. Dave's house is **more beautiful**.

   Los Angeles is **expensive**. San Francisco is **more expensive**.

   Remember, we don't say, ~~San Francisco is more expensiver~~.

6. We add than when we say the person or thing we are comparing.

   Ana's apartment is **smaller than Kate's apartment**.

   Los Angeles is **more expensive than San Francisco**.

   This apartment is **hotter than my old apartment**.

7. To show a small difference when we make comparisons, we can use a little. To show a big difference, we can use much.

   Luis:　　Your apartment is **a little bigger** than my apartment.

   Chris: I know, but your bedroom is **much bigger**.

8. Some common adjectives have irregular forms.

   good—better
   bad—worse

   Your apartment has a **better** view than my apartment does.

   The weather is bad today, but yesterday it was **worse**.

Grammar 2: Similarities and Differences: As . . . as

1. To show that people, places, or things are the same in some way, we use as before and after an adjective.

   Paul:　How's the weather today?

   Laura: It's **as cold as** yesterday.

   This means that yesterday it was cold. Today it is also cold.

   Clara: How old are you, Ana?

   Ana:　I'm 25. My birthday was on April 1st. I'm **as old as** you, I think.

   Clara: Funny. I thought you were younger.

   This means that Clara and Ana are 25 years old.

2. We can add just to emphasize that 2 things are the same.

   Kate's apartment is **just as big as** Sam's apartment.

3. When we want to show that 2 people, places, or things are very similar in some way but not exactly the same, we can add almost.

   Frankie: I'm **almost as old as** you.

   Sara:　You are not. You're only 12. I'm 13.

4. To compare 2 people, places, or things and show that they are different, we use not as . . . as.

   Frankie and Maggie are**n't as old as** Ana.

   This means that Ana is older than Frankie and Maggie.

   Paul:　Emi is so shy sometimes.

   Laura: She is**n't as shy as** Maggie!

   This means that Maggie is shyer than Emi.

   Kate:　Is Mexico City expensive?

   Luis:　Mexico City is expensive, but it's **not as expensive as** Tokyo.

   This means that Tokyo is more expensive.

Grammar 3: Comparing Nouns

1. We use like to compare people, places, or things. Here are examples of like in statements, yes/no questions, and information questions. We use like to show that a noun is similar to another noun.

   Chris: **Mr. Arnello** is like **Mr. Jackson**.

   Ana:　Yes, they both like to cook.

   Emi:　Is **your new apartment like your old one**?

   Kate:　I don't have a new apartment. I'm looking for one now.

   Frankie: What's Tokyo like?

   Emi:　**Tokyo** is a lot **like New York**.

2. We can also use *both* to show that 2 people or things are similar.

> **Both men** like to cook.
> London is like Tokyo. **Both cities** are very interesting.

3. When the 2 things we compare are the same, we use *the same* or *the same as*.

> **Laura:** Emi and Jin are in **the same** class.
> **Paul:** What time is the class?
>
> **Laura:** Emi has **the same** teacher as Jin.
> **Paul:** Professor Brown? That's good.

4. We can use *different from* to talk about things that are not the same.

> Professor Brown is **different from** Mrs. Hayes.
> Professor Brown is funny, but Mrs. Hayes is serious.

C.3 Somewhere Around Here

Listening

🎧 **A. Listen to Track 25.** *Luis and Kate are talking about where they're from. Fill in the chart.*

	Luis	Kate
Father is from		
Mother is from		
Born in		

🎧 **B. Listen to Track 26.** *A tour guide is giving a tour of San Francisco. Organize the tour guide's notes. Match the facts to each place.*

1. Union Square __b__ , _____	a. can see great views of the bay from here
2. The Fairmont Hotel _____	b. major shops and department stores
3. Grace Cathedral _____ , _____	c. modeled after Notre Dame Cathedral
4. The top of Nob Hill _____	d. public park since 1861
	e. built in 1928
	f. presidents and kings stay here

Vocabulary

Study Tip
Write vocabulary words from the course on Post-it notes. Put the notes where you will see them every day.

A. Complete the sentences. Use the words in the box.

beaches	deserts	forests	mountains	oceans	rivers

1. Kilimanjaro and Everest are both famous _____.

2. The Pacific and the Atlantic are two large _____.

3. Redwood National Park and Sequoia National Park are large _____ in the United States, with thousands of huge trees.

4. The Amazon and the Nile are two famous _____.

5. The Sahara in Africa and the Great Victoria in Australia are two of the world's largest _____.

6. Copacabana, in Brazil, and Acapulco, in Mexico, are two of the world's most beautiful _____.

B. For each natural feature, name the one that's nearest to where you live.

The nearest beach: _____

The nearest ocean: _____

The nearest forest: _____

The nearest river: _____

The nearest mountain: _____

The nearest desert: _____

Grammar 1

Superlatives

A. *Complete the conversations. Use the superlative form of the adjectives in the box. Be sure to use* **the** *if needed.*

good	slow	strange	hot	fast	delicious
young	old	boring	long		

1. **Frankie:** Dad, what's ___the slowest___ animal in the world?

   Paul: Probably the tortoise or the sloth. They're both really slow. I know that _____ mammal is the cheetah. It can run at over 70 miles an hour.

2. **Susan:** What's _____ holiday you've had, Laura?

   Laura: Oh, last year we went to Rio de Janeiro. It was wonderful. And it was also _____ place I've ever been—it was over 95 degrees (40 degrees Centigrade) every day.

3. **Sam:** What's _____ food you've eaten, Emi?

   Emi: I once had sheep's eyeballs. That was really weird.

4. **Emi:** What is your favorite kind of food?

   Sam: Oh, Turkish, definitely. I think Turkish food is _____ food in the world.

5. **Kate:** What's _____ flight you've had, Chris?

   Chris: Paris to Australia. It was more than 24 hours, I think. It was also _____ flight, because my headphones didn't work and I had nothing to read!

6. **Lucy:** Who's _____ person in your family, Emi?

   Emi: Oh, you won't believe this, but my great-great-grandmother, Gin Okada, is still alive. She's 103! And my niece, Rika Okada, is _____. She's only 6 months old.

B. *Write questions for these travel quiz answers from the* Guinness Book of World Records. *Make a superlative from the adjectives in list A and choose the correct word from list B.*

A	fast	popular	old	busy	high	long
B	railway	road	bicycle speed	tourist spot	road	hotel

1. <u>What is the world's fastest bicycle speed?</u>

It's 160 miles (268 kilometers) per hour. The cyclist was Dutchman Fred Rompelberg, and the record ride was in the United States in 1995.

2. _____

It's the East Japan Railway Company. Around 16 million passengers take its trains every day.

3. _____

It's France. In 2001, over 76 million tourists visited the country (the population is only 60 million).

4. _____

It's the Pan-American Highway. It runs from Alaska to Brasilia—over 15,000 miles (25,000 kilometers).

5. _____

It's the Khardungla Pass in Kashmir, India. At its highest point, it's over 5,682 meters (18,640 feet).

6. _____

It's the Hoshi Ryokan, a hotel in Awazu, Japan. It was first built in the year 717, and it now has 100 rooms.

Grammar 2

Definite and Indefinite Articles and No Article

Complete the paragraph. Fill in the missing articles. Use **a**, **an**, **the**, *or* ∅.

Copacabana in (1)_____ Rio de Janeiro is one of (2)_____ world's (3)_____ most famous beaches. (4)_____ visitors can learn a lot about (5)_____ Brazilian life when they walk along (6)_____ beach. There is so much to watch. You will see local teenagers playing *futevolei*, which is (7)_____ mix of (8)_____ soccer and (9)_____ volleyball. You will see (10)_____ surfers who are trying to surf (11)_____ biggest waves. And of course you will see many people standing around talking to each other.

Every few minutes, somebody will try to sell you (12)_____ something—(13)_____ ice-cold drink, some suntan lotion, or perhaps (14)_____ necklace made of (15)_____ shells. If you're lucky, you'll even be able to attend (16)_____ free music show or (17)_____ sports event, right there on (18)_____ beach.

Grammar 3

Review of Pronouns, Possessive Nouns, and Possessive Adjectives

Identify the error in each conversation. Circle the letter of the error and write the correction in the blank. If there is no error, write OK.

1. **Ana:** I have a pretty small family. <u>My</u> parents had 3 children. Do <u>you</u> have
   (A)   (B)

   a big family?

   Kate: <u>Mine</u> is small, too. I have just one sister. <u>She's</u> lives in New York.
   (C)   (D)

   1. _____

2. **Ana:** <u>Luis's</u> Spanish is perfect. Is <u>he</u> from Mexico?
   (A)   (B)

   Kate: No, <u>his</u> parents are from Mexico, but <u>he</u> was born in the United States.
   (C)   (D)

   2. _____

3. **Ilya:** Hey, Jin, can I borrow <u>your</u> history book? <u>Mine</u> book is at home.
   (A)   (B)

   Jin: Sure, I don't need <u>it</u>. <u>My</u> history class is finished.
   (C) (D)

   3. _____

Application Activities

1. **Vocabulary.** Build your vocabulary. Find a picture of a mountain, a beach, a forest, a desert, and a river. Write down all the adjectives and nouns that you can think of when you look at each picture.

2. **Grammar.** Find a list of world records. Write down 5 interesting questions (for example, *What is the longest . . . ?*) and the answers. Show your questions to a friend. Does your friend know the answers?

3. **Writing.** Give a tour of the city you live in or the place you are in now. Write a script for your tour. Be sure to mention the busiest / oldest / newest / most popular / most famous places. Use the script for Track 26 as a model (see the Audioscript at the back of the book).

4. **Speaking.** Describe your country or a country you have visited. What are the best and worst things about it? How beautiful are the natural places? What is your favorite place, and why?

5. **Project.** Choose an ecotour. Find a brochure or a website that describes "natural tours." Make a list of 10 activities you can do on the tour. Give a presentation to your class.

Grammar Explanations

This section contains the same grammar explanations that are found on the CD-ROM. They are included here for your quick reference. To view the animated presentation, go to the Grammar section of Unit C.3 in the CD-ROM course.

Grammar 1: Superlatives

1. We use the superlative form of adjectives to compare 3 or more people, places, or things.
   Luis: Colima is **the most beautiful** place on Earth!
   Kate: I'd like to see it some day.

2. To form the superlatives of short adjectives, we add *the* before the adjective and *-est* to the end of the adjective. When the adjective ends in *e*, add *-st*.
   Mount Everest is **the highest** mountain.
   California has **the tallest** trees.
   Canada has **the nicest** people.

   When the adjective ends in a vowel and a single consonant, we usually double the consonant and add *-est*.
   Mexico City is the **biggest** city in my country.
   The Sahara desert is the **hottest** place in the world.

3. When an adjective ends in *y*, we usually change the *y* to *i* and add *-est* to form the superlative.
   New York is a very busy city.
   I think it's the **busiest** city in the United States.

4. Adjectives with irregular comparative forms also have irregular superlative forms.
   Chris gives **good** presentations.
   Clara's presentations are a little **better**. (comparative)
   Ana's presentations are the **best**! (superlative)

   Laura is a **bad** cook.
   Maggie is **worse**. (comparative)
   Frankie is the **worst**. (superlative)

5. Adjectives with 2 or more syllables use *the most* with the adjective to make the superlative. The adjective does not change.
   Colima is **the most beautiful** place on Earth.
   Remember, we don't say, ~~the most beautifulest~~.

Grammar 2: Definite and Indefinite Articles and No Article

1. We use the indefinite articles *a* or *an* before singular count nouns and before adjectives with singular count nouns.
   Emily: I live in **an apartment**.
   Student: Do you like it?
   Emily: A lot—there's **a beautiful park** and **a great coffee shop** on the corner.

2. We don't use *a* or *an* with non-count nouns or plural nouns. We use *some* or no article when we are not talking about specific things.
   Luis: Colima has **some** beautiful **beaches**.
   Kate: I'd like to see them. I love **beaches**.
   Luis: I do, too.

   Kate means beaches in general.

3. We use *the* when we think a person, place, or thing is unique or the best.
   Luis: Colima is **the most beautiful place** on Earth!
   Kate: No, California is **the most beautiful place** on Earth!

4. We use the definite article *the* with both count nouns and non-count nouns. We use *the* when we are talking about specific things that the speaker and listener know about.
   Luis: I really like **the beaches** near Colima.
   Kate: I like **the beaches** in California.

5. We also use *the* with names of famous places, oceans, rivers, mountains, and regions.
   the Museum of Modern Art
   the Pacific Ocean
   the Amazon
   the Himalayas
   the Middle East

6. We don't usually use *the* with names of countries, continents, or cities.
   Colima is in Mexico.
   Mexico City is the capital of Mexico.
   I'd like to visit South America.

   But we do use *the* with these countries:
   the United Kingdom (the UK)
   the United States (the US)
   the United Arab Emirates (the UAE)
   the People's Republic of China (the PRC)

7. We use *the* for specific places and things that are clear to the speaker and listener.
   Jin: Did you do **the homework**?
   Emi: Yes, I gave it to Professor Brown.

   Jin: I'll meet you in **the library**.
   Emi: No, let's meet in **the cafeteria**.

Grammar 3: Review of Pronouns, Possessive Nouns, and Possessive Adjectives

1. There are three kinds of pronouns in English: subject pronouns, object pronouns, and possessive pronouns. First, let's review subject pronouns.

    Luis is from Colima.
    He is from Colima.

    He is a subject pronoun. *He* means *Luis* in this sentence.

    Kate: Luis, where are **you** from?
    Luis: San Francisco. **You** know that.

Subject Pronouns	
Singular	**Plural**
I	we
you	you
he, she, it	they

2. Next, let's review object pronouns.
    Kate knows Luis.
    Kate knows **him**.

    Remember, in this sentence, *him* is the object pronoun. *Him* means *Luis*. Object pronouns follow the verb.

    Kate: Where is Colima?
    Luis: Here, let me show **you**.

Object Pronouns	
Singular	**Plural**
I	us
you	you
him, her, it	them

3. Now let's talk about possessive nouns, adjectives, and pronouns. They show that something belongs to us. We form possessive nouns by adding an apostrophe and *-s*.
    Luis
    Luis**'s**
    Luis**'s** family lived in Mexico.

    His sisters
    His sisters**'** bedroom
    His sisters**'** bedroom was beautiful.

4. Possessive adjectives are like possessive nouns.
    Luis's family is from Mexico.
    His family is from Mexico.

    Luis's sisters are in Los Angeles.
    His sisters are in Los Angeles.

    His is a possessive adjective. *His* means *Luis's* in this sentence.

    Kate's family is from California.
    Her family is from California.

    Her is a possessive adjective, too.
    Her means *Kate's* in this sentence.

Possessive Adjectives	
Singular	**Plural**
my	our
you	your
his, her, its	their

5. Finally, let's learn about possessive pronouns.
    Luis: My family is from Mexico.
    Ana: **Mine** is from Brazil.

    Mine is a possessive pronoun. *Mine* means *my family* in this sentence.

6. Look at these examples of possessive adjectives and possessive pronouns:
    This isn't **my** office. **Mine** is down the hall.
    This isn't **your** folder. **Yours** is in your office.
    I don't have **his** laptop. **His** is on his desk.
    I don't have **her** calculator. **Hers** is on the table.
    This isn't **our** office. **Ours** in on the ninth floor.
    These aren't **your** folders. **Yours** are on the floor.
    That's not **their** office. **Theirs** is across the hall.

    Remember, we never use a noun after a possessive pronoun. We don't say, ~~Mine office is down the hall.~~

7. Notice the verb that follows a possessive pronoun.
    Her notebook is at home. (singular)
    Hers **is** at home.
    Her notebooks are at home. (plural)
    Hers **are** at home.

C.4 It's Spicy!

🎧 **A. Listen to Track 27.** *Sam and Emi are eating at a restaurant in Japan. Fill in the missing phrases in the dialog.*

Sam: (1)_____ this little dish?

Emi: That's the *sashimishoyuzara*.

Sam: (2)_____?

Emi: It's a dish (3)_____ for the

soy sauce.

Sam: Oh. And this is the soy sauce,

(4)_____?

Emi: Mm-hmmm.

Sam: And (5)_____ green stuff?

Emi: It's called *wasabi*.

Sam: *Wasabi?*

Emi: Mm-hmmm. It's like horseradish. It's a spice (6)_____

with the soy sauce.

Sam: I'll try it.

Emi: Careful. It's very spicy.

Sam: Good. I love spicy food.

Emi: Wait, wait, wait!

Sam: Wow, that is spicy!

Emi: Here, drink some water . . . (7)_____?

Sam: Whew! Yeah, I'm OK. Next time, I won't eat the whole thing.

Emi: Sam, you're supposed to *mix* it with the soy sauce!

BONUS

Have you ever been surprised when you tried a new food? What was the food? Why were you surprised?

🎧 **B. Listen to Track 28.** *Kate is asking Luis for a recipe. Write down the ingredients for* ceviche.

- some _____, like s_____ b_____
- _____ oil
- _____ juice
- t_____
- o_____

BONUS
Why doesn't Luis tell Kate how to make the sauce?

_____

Vocabulary

A. *Match the words and definitions.*

_____ **1.** guidebook   **a.** a book that describes places and activities

_____ **2.** sightseeing   **b.** a famous building or monument that's often in the middle of a city

_____ **3.** landmark   **c.** a small card that has a picture on it

_____ **4.** souvenir   **d.** a short trip through a city

_____ **5.** postcard   **e.** something that you buy to remind you of something

_____ **6.** tour   **f.** visiting famous or interesting places on vacation

B. *Now complete the sentences. Use the words in Exercise A.*

1. **Kate:** I'm going to Paris next week for a holiday.

     Luis: Please be sure to send me a _____.

2. **Clara:** Wow. It's our first day in Paris. What should we do?

     Kate: Let's go _____. There are so many interesting places to see!

3. **Clara:** What's that over there?

     Maggie: Oh, that's the Arc de Triomphe. It's a famous

         _____ in the city.

4. **Janet:** How do we get to the Eiffel Tower?

     Kate: I'm not sure. Let's look in our _____.

5. **Kate:** I want to see everything! Let's take a _____.

   Clara: Good idea. How about a _____ by boat? It goes down the Seine River.

6. **Clara:** Oh, look! I'm going to buy this little statue. This will be a great _____.

   Kate: Oh, Clara! Only tourists buy things like that!

Grammar 1

Review of Questions

Complete the conversations. Use the questions in the box. Capitalize as necessary.

how does it work	how big is it	what's it for	how old is it
what does it look like	how much is it	what's this	what is it

Maggie: Mom, (1)_____?

Laura: It's a garlic press.

Maggie: (2)_____?

Laura: It's used for squeezing juice from garlic.

Maggie: (3)_____?

Laura: It's easy. You just put the garlic in the top. Then you squeeze the handles.

Maggie: It looks kind of old. (4)_____?

Laura: I'm not sure, but it's pretty old. Your grandmother gave it to me.

Laura: Paul, when you go to the grocery store, please get me a new apple slicer.

Paul: An apple slicer? (5)_____?

Laura: It's a kind of knife. It's used for cutting apples.

Paul: (6)_____?

Laura: It has 2 small handles and about 12 small blades.

Paul: (7)_____?

Laura: It's not big. Its about 4 inches wide and 6 inches long.

Paul: All right. I'll look for one. (8)_____?

Laura: It's not expensive. Maybe $2 or $3.

Grammar 2

Relative Pronouns and Relative Clauses

A. *Complete the definitions. Circle the correct word.*

1. *Sushi* is a Japanese food **it's /(that's)/ who's** made with fresh fish and rice.

2. The *sushino itamae* is the person **which / he / who** cuts the fish and prepares the food.

3. *Ceviche* is a kind of Latin American dish **who / what / that** is made from fish, tomatoes, onions, olive oil, and lime juice.

4. *Antipasti* is food **it / which / who** is served as a starter in Italian meals.

5. A *maître d'* is the person **they / which / who** is in charge of the other waiters in a restaurant.

B. *Read the definitions in Exercise A again. Write questions for each answer.*

1. _____What is a Japanese food that's made with fresh fish and rice?_____

   Answer: Sushi.

2. _____

   Answer: A maitre d'.

3. _____

   Answer: Antipasti.

C. *Match the pairs of sentences. Then make each pair into one sentence by connecting with* **who,** **which,** *or* **that.** *Remember to change* **a** *to* **the** *if necessary.*

_____ **1.** Peter Jackson is a New Zealander.

_____ **2.** Athens is a European city.

_____ **3.** J. K. Rowling is a British author.

_____ **4.** Chinese New Year is a major holiday.

_____ **5.** Aung San Suu Kyi is a Burmese leader.

a. Ms. Rowling wrote the Harry Potter novels.

b. It is celebrated by Chinese people around the world.

c. Mr. Jackson directed *The Lord of the Rings.*

d. Ms. Suu Kyi won the Nobel Peace Prize.

e. Athens hosted the 2004 Summer Olympics.

1. _____Peter Jackson is the New Zealander who directed *The Lord of the Rings.*_____

2. _____

3. _____

4. _____

5. _____

Tag Questions

Complete the conversations. Use the correct tag question.

Maggie: Mom, it's OK if I go to a school dance tomorrow night, (1)_____isn't it_____?

Laura: Well, I guess so. You're not going to stay out late, (2)_____?

Maggie: No, Mom. I'll be back early. I promise.

Kate: I'm planning to have a dinner party on Saturday. You'll be here, (3)_____?

Luis: No, I won't. I'll be out of town this weekend.

Kate: Then I'll change the party to the 25th. That's OK, (4)_____?

Luis: Sure, that's fine.

Maggie: Frankie! You ate the ice cream in the freezer, (5)_____?

Frankie: Um, yes, I ate it. That wasn't yours, (6)_____?

Maggie: Yes, it *was* mine.

Frankie: Sorry. I didn't know that.

Maggie: Emi's going back to Japan next week, (7)_____?

Laura: That's right. We're really going to miss her, (8)_____?

Maggie: Yes. I know I will!

Application Activities

Study Tip
Choose 3 troublesome grammar points. Look them up in the Grammar Reference. Say the example sentences.

1. **Vocabulary.** Find a new recipe from another culture. Make 2 lists of vocabulary: (1) the ingredients (nouns) that are used in the recipe and (2) the actions (verbs) for preparing it.

2. **Writing.** Keep a food diary for a week. Write down the different foods you eat. Look up new words in a dictionary. At the end of the week, write a short report on your eating habits. Compare your report with those of your classmates.

3. **Speaking.** Talk about one of your favorite dishes that is typical in your family or in your country.

4. **Project.** Find out about a festival in another country. Find a guidebook or go to a travel website. Choose a festival and get information to answer questions like these: *What kind of festival is it? When does it take place? What happens at the festival?* Give a short presentation to your class.

Grammar Explanations

This section contains the same grammar explanations that are found on the CD-ROM. They are included here for your quick reference. To view the animated presentation, go to the Grammar section of Unit C.4 in the CD-ROM course.

Grammar 1: Review of Questions

1. We use *who* for questions about people.
   Clara: **Who's giving** this presentation?
   Luis: Susan Wu is giving it.
   This question asks about the subject of the action.
   Clara: **Who does** she **report** to?
   Luis: She reports to Laura.
   This question asks about the object of the action.

   Remember, we don't use *do*, *does*, or *did* when *who* is used to ask a question about the subject. Notice the form of the verb.
   Emily: **Who wants** a bigger office?
   Students: Luis does.
   Emily: **Who wants** a new laptop?
   Students: Clara and Luis do.

2. We use *what* for questions about things.
   Clara: **What's that?**
   Luis: It's Susan's new laptop.
   Paul: **What have** you **done** today?
   Frankie: I haven't done a lot. It was a boring day.

   Remember, there are 2 ways to form questions with *what*. We can ask questions about objects of verbs, or we can ask questions about the subjects of verbs.
   Paul: **What does** that little boy **want**?
   Laura: He wants some cookies.
   Paul: **What costs** the most?
   Laura: The Chocolate Crunch costs the most, I think.

3. We use *what kind* to get more information about something.
   Laura: **What kind** of ice cream do you want?
   Frankie: Chocolate Crunch!

4. We use *what time* to ask about time.
   Chris: **What time** does the movie start?
   Kate: At 8:00.

5. We also use *when* to ask about time.
   Chris: **When** does the movie start?
   Kate: At 8:00.

6. We use *where* to ask about locations.
   Luis: **Where** are you going tonight?
   Kate: To the Rock. Do you want to come?

7. There are many kinds of questions we can ask using *how*.
   • We can ask for directions.
     Luis: **How** do I get to Lucid?
     Laura: Take College Avenue to Ashby and turn right.

• We can ask about quantities. With count nouns, we use *how many*.
  Dave: **How many** pickles do you want?
  Emi: Just 1, please.

• With non-count nouns, we use *how much*.
  Laura: **How much** ice cream do you want?
  Frankie: A very big bowl.

Grammar 2: Relative Pronouns and Relative Clauses

1. We use a subject relative clause to give more information about people, places, or things.
   I have a friend **who comes from Japan**.
   Japan is a country **that has an interesting history**.

2. Relative clauses help us make 2 sentences into 1.
   I have a friend. She comes from Japan.
   I have a friend **who** comes from Japan.

   Japan is a country. It has an interesting history.
   Japan is a country **that** has an interesting history.

3. Subject relative clauses begin with subject relative pronouns.
   • *Who* and *that* are relative pronouns. We use *who* and *that* with people.
     Emi is a student. She is studying English.
     Emi is a student **who** is studying English.
     Emi is a student **that** is studying English.

   Note: *Who* and *that* are the subjects of these relative clauses.

   • We use *that* with places or things.
     Marshmallows is a movie. It is really funny.
     Marshmallows is a movie **that** is really funny.

     This is a sushi bar. It's always crowded.
     This is a sushi bar **that** is always crowded.

4. Relative pronouns have only 1 form. They have the same form for women and men and for singular and plural nouns.
   Emi is a student **who** studies every day.
   Jin is a student **who** doesn't study every day.
   Yoko and Jose are students **who** don't study at all.

5. The verb in the relative clause is singular when the subject relative pronoun goes with a singular noun. When the subject relative pronoun goes with a plural noun, it is plural.
   Emily is a **teacher** who **loves** to teach online.
   Emily and Professor Brown are **teachers** who **love** to teach online.

Grammar 3: Tag Questions

1. We use tag questions to check information that we think is true. We form tag questions like this:

- We begin with a statement:
  It's a nice day.

- And we add a tag.
  . . . isn't it?
  It's a nice day, **isn't it?**

  Emi: It's a nice day, **isn't it?**
  Student: Yes, it is.
  Emi: You're ready to begin the lesson, **aren't you?**
  Student: Yes, I am.
  Sam: You like spicy food, **don't you?**
  Emi: Yes, I really do.

2. When the statement verb is affirmative, the tag verb is negative.

  Emily: It's a nice day today, **isn't it?**
  Student: Yes, it is.
  Emi: You work on weekends, **don't you?**
  Dave: Yes, I do.

3. When the statement has a form of the verb *be*, we use the same form of *be* in the tag.

  Sam: This **is** the soy sauce, **isn't it?**
  Emi: Yes, it is.
  Sam: And these **are** my chopsticks, **aren't they?**
  Emi: Yes, they are.

  Ana: Emi's going to Kate's party, **isn't she?**
  Chris: Yes, she is.

  Ana: You **were** here last night, **weren't you?**
  Chris: Yes, I was.

Remember, we always use a pronoun in the tag. We say, *Emi's going to the party, isn't she?* We don't say, ~~*Emi's going to the party, isn't Emi?*~~

4. When the statement is in the simple present tense, we use *don't* or *doesn't* in the tag.

  Emi: You **work** on weekends, **don't** you?
  Dave: Yes, I do. I work 7 days a week!

  Emi: Rich **works** on weekends, too, **doesn't** he?
  Dave: Yes, he does.
  Emi: Karen and Charlie **work** on weekends, **don't** they?
  Dave: Yes, they do.

5. When the statement is in the simple past tense, we use *didn't* in the tag.

  Emi: You **wanted** to come here, **didn't** you?
  Sam: Yes, I did. I wanted to try Japanese food.

  Sam: Ana and Chris **ate** here last week, **didn't** they?
  Emi: Yes, they did. Ana loves Japanese food.

6. When the statement is negative, notice the tag verb. It is not negative.

  Emily: It **wasn't** very nice yesterday, **was** it?
  Student: No, it wasn't.

  Emi: You **don't** like Japanese food, **do** you?
  Sam: No, I don't. Sorry.

7. We answer a tag question the same as a *yes-no* question. We can use a short answer or a long answer.

  Dave: You're getting tired, aren't you?
  Emi: **Yes, I am.**
  Sam: He isn't here, is he?
  Kate: **No. He's going to be late.**

C.5 You Gotta Do It!

Listening

🎧 **A. Listen to Track 29.** *Ana is telling Chris some news. Fill in the missing phrases in the dialog.*

Ana: Have you (1)_____?

Chris: Heard what?

Ana: I got a job offer from Media View.

Chris: Really? From Media View. Where are they?

Ana: London.

Chris: Wow, that's great. Have you (2)_____ to London?

Ana: No, I've (3)_____ to England, period.

Chris: Well, what are you (4)_____ do?

Ana: I think you know . . .

Ana and Chris (together): You gotta do what you gotta do!

Chris: So you're (5)_____ take it?

Ana: Yeah, I just can't pass this up.

Chris: Have (6)_____ Mr. Arnello?

Ana: Yep, I (7)_____ him this morning, and he totally (8)_____.

Chris: Well, what (9)_____ going to do there?

Ana: I'm (10)_____ Assistant Art Director. It's a big step up for me.

Chris: Wow, great! When do you start?

Ana: Next month. I can't wait. London!

Chris: Well, Ana, I'm really happy for you. We're going to miss you around here!

🎧 **B. Listen to Track 30.** *Ana is calling Mr. Jones at Media View in London. Answer the questions below. Fill in the letter of the correct expression.*

_____ **1.** How does Ana ask for Mr. Jones?

_____ **2.** How does she tell him her decision?

_____ **3.** How does she explain her decision?

_____ **4.** How does Mr. Jones identify himself?

_____ **5.** How does he greet Ana?

_____ **6.** How does he show how happy he is about her decision?

_____ **7.** How does he tell Ana the next step she must take?

a. I've decided to accept the offer.

b. Yes, I've thought it over carefully, and I'm sure it's the right thing to do.

c. Oh, Ana, how are you?

d. Could I speak with Andrew Jones, please?

e. That's wonderful! I'm very pleased to hear that.

f. Hello. This is Andrew Jones.

g. Let me connect you with our human resources person, and we'll get this all sorted out for you.

Vocabulary

Kate is interviewing Su-Lin for a new job at I-Travel. Replace the underlined words in the interview on the next page with words from the box.

Job posting
New position.
Full-time Reservations Assistant.
Starting $18/hour.
Contact Kate Taylor at I-Travel.
415-555-0987

reference	interview	excellent	hired me	job title
get a promotion	paycheck	payment	raise	résumé

Kate: OK, Ms. Chang. Thanks for coming to this <u>meeting about the job</u>.
interview
1.

Su-Lin: My pleasure.

Kate: I have your <u>description of work experience</u> here. <u>Very impressive</u>
2.   3.
background.

Su-Lin: Thank you. I love what I do.

Kate: Have you worked with the Apollo reservations system before?

Su-Lin: Oh, yes. When World Travel <u>gave me a job</u>, I was trained on it.
4.

Kate: What's your <u>position</u> at World Travel?
5.

Su-Lin: Now I'm a "reservation specialist." I help people make reservations. I've
had this job for 6 months.

Kate: I see. Well, do you have any questions for me?

Su-Lin: Yes, I do. I know what <u>salary</u> you offer, but is it possible that I might get a
6.
<u>pay increase</u> in my first year?
7.

Kate: Yes, there's a pay increase every May. Now, I should tell you that we have
to contact your current employer for a <u>report on your performance</u>. I hope
8.
that's OK.

Su-Lin: Sure. That's no problem.

Kate: Well, thanks for coming in today.

Su-Lin: Thank you.

Grammar 1

Present Perfect

A. *Complete the sentences. Use the present perfect form of the verb in parentheses.*

1. Maggie **(have)** ___has had___ her pet snake, Boris, since she was 10 years old.

2. I **(know)** _____ Jin since the first day of school. He's become a really good friend.

3. What a long meeting! Paul and Chris **(be)** _____ in that room for 4 hours.

4. Sam left around noon. He **(not be)** _____ here for about 3 hours.

5. I **(not see)** _____ my family since February. I really miss them!

6. I really need a vacation. I **(not go)** _____ anywhere for a long, long time.

B. *Write sentences about yourself or about people you know. Use the present perfect. Write 2 positive and 2 negative sentences. Here are some ideas:* **like** *(a sport or a food),* **speak** *(a language),* **know** *(someone),* **know how** *(to do something),* **live** *(somewhere),* **be** *(somewhere),* **see** *(someone),* **do** *(something).*

1. _____ for a long, long time.

2. _____ since I was _____ years old.

3. (Use *not.*) _____ since _____.

4. (Use *not.*) _____ for about _____.

Grammar 2

Present Perfect and Past Tense

A. *Complete the sentences. Use the simple past or present perfect form of the verbs in parentheses. Sometimes 2 answers are possible.*

1. **(see, rent)** We ___'ve seen___ this film before. Don't you remember? We _____ it last month.

2. **(live, move)** I love New York. I _____ here all my life. My family _____ here in the 1950s.

3. **(buy, always like)** Do you like this blue sweater? We _____ it yesterday for Karen's birthday. She _____ the color blue ever since she was a little girl.

4. **(not clean, not do)** Just a minute, Frankie! You _____ your room. You _____ any housework for over a month!

5. **(always go, decide)** The Arnellos _____ to Florida for their summer vacation. This year they _____ to go to Mexico for a change.

B. *Complete the sentences. Use the correct form of the verbs in the box. Sometimes both the simple past and present perfect are correct. Use the present perfect if possible.*

find	break	bring	buy	lose	miss	have	leave	drop

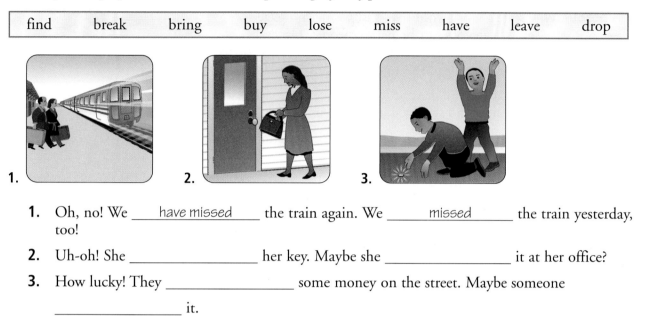

1.   2.   3.

1. Oh, no! We _____have missed_____ the train again. We _____missed_____ the train yesterday, too!

2. Uh-oh! She _____ her key. Maybe she _____ it at her office?

3. How lucky! They _____ some money on the street. Maybe someone _____ it.

Grammar 3

Review of Verb Tenses

Complete the profile of actress Keira Knightley. Use the correct form of the verb in parentheses.

Keira Knightley is part of a new generation of British actors. She has now
(1)_____ **(become)** as famous as anyone in Hollywood.

Keira (2)_____ **(be)** born in the south of England in March
1985. She (3)_____ **(appear)** in her first film when she
(4)_____ **(be)** only seven, and she (5)_____ already
_____ **(make)** more than 20 films.

As a young teenager, she (6)_____ **(want)** to be a dancer, but
her life (7)_____ **(change)** when she (8)_____ **(win)** a part in the film
Star Wars at the age of 12.

Keira (9)_____ **(not go)** to college. However, she (10)_____**(do)** well
in her "A Level" (final) exams in high school, even though she (11)_____ **(play)** her
first big role in *Bend It Like Beckham* at the same time.

Now, since her roles in *Dr. Zhivago, Love Actually, King Arthur,* and the *Pirates of the Caribbean,*
she (12)_____ **(be)** one of Britain's biggest screen stars.

Application Activities

Study Tip
Review! Look back through the units. Review at least 10 of the exercises and 5 of the Application Activities.

1. **Vocabulary.** Create a work word tree. List words connected to jobs. Use several categories or branches: people / places / what the job involves / pay and benefits. Compare your word tree with those of your classmates. Add new words and expressions.

2. **Writing.** Write a description of your ideal job. Describe what job it is, why you are interested in it, and why you are the right person for the job.

3. **Speaking.** Ask someone about his or her job. Ask questions like these: *What do you do? What is your schedule? What do you like about your job?* (Note: We don't usually ask people about their salary!)

4. **Project.** Go to a job site on the Internet. Choose a category, then find a job in it. Take notes on what the job is, location, salary, and any other details. Report your findings to the class.

Grammar Explanations

This section contains the same grammar explanations that are found on the CD-ROM. They are included here for your quick reference. To view the animated presentation, go to the Grammar section of Unit C.5 in the CD-ROM course.

Grammar 1: Present Perfect

1. We use the present perfect to talk about things that happened in the past. When we use the present perfect, we don't know when something happened or the time is not important.
   > I've **been** to Europe.
   > I've **visited** Europe several times.

2. To form the present perfect, we use *have* or *has* and the past participle of a verb. The past participle of regular verbs is the same as the simple past form.
   > Luis **has** always **loved** tennis.
   > Emi and Kate **have** never **wanted** to play tennis.
   > I **have visited** Europe several times.

3.

The Present Perfect	
Singular	
I have walked	I've walked
you have walked	you've walked
she has walked	she's walked
he has walked	he's walked
it has walked	it's walked
Emi has walked	Emi's walked
Plural	
we have walked	we've walked
you have walked	you've walked
they have walked	they've walked

Remember, the contracted form of *have* is *'ve*. The contraction for *has* is *'s*.

4. Irregular verbs have special past participles. Here are some common ones:

Simple Form: Past Participle	
be—been	make—made
come—come	say—said
do—done	send—sent
eat—eaten	teach—taught
go—gone	tell—told
have—had	think—thought
know—known	write—written

5. To make the negative, put *not* after *have* or *has*. We can also use the contractions *haven't* or *hasn't*.
   > I **have not** been to Mexico.
   > I **haven't** been to Mexico.

   > Ana **has not** met Luis's family.
   > Ana **hasn't** met Luis's family.

6. To make a *yes/no* question, we change the order like this:
   > Ana has told Mr. Arnello the good news.
   > **Has** Ana **told** Mr. Arnello the good news?

7. We can use *ever* with the present perfect to ask questions.
   > **Chris:** **Have** you **ever been** to London?
   > **Ana:** No, I've never been to England.
   > **Dave:** **Has** Emi **ever made** sushi for you?
   > **Kate:** No, she never has.

8. We can answer with a long answer or a short answer. The short answer is more common in conversations. Use *have* or *has* in the short answer.
   > **Kate:** Has Kate told Mr. Arnello about her new job?
   > **Chris:** **Yes, she told him yesterday.**
   > **Kate:** Have Tom and Clara heard about Ana's new job?
   > **Chris:** **No, they haven't.**

   Remember, we don't use contractions in the affirmative short answer. We say, *Yes, I have.* We don't say, ~~*Yes, I've.*~~

9. To make information questions, put the question words before *have* or *has* like this:
   > **Laura:** **What** assignments **have** you finished?
   > **Frankie:** Most of my math problems and my Spanish composition.

   > **Laura:** **Who have** you called?
   > **Maggie:** Brian and Mary.

   > **Laura:** **Where has** all the ice cream gone?
   > **Paul:** Maggie and her friends ate it.

10. Notice the difference in these questions with *who* and *what*.
    > **Laura:** What assignment have you finished?
    > **Frankie:** I've finished most of my Spanish composition.

    > **Laura:** What has taken so much time?
    > **Frankie:** Well, my math assignment took a lot of time.

    > **Laura:** Who have you called?
    > **Maggie:** I called Brian and Mary.

    > **Laura:** Who has called?
    > **Maggie:** Dr. Lee and Mrs. Smith called.

Grammar 2: Present Perfect and Past Tense

1. Remember, we use the present perfect when we don't know or don't want to be specific about when something happened in the past.
    Chris: Ana **has been** to Los Angeles.
    Luis: Yes, I know.
    Ana: I**'ve told** Mr. Arnello about my job offer.
    Chris: Really?

    We use the simple past tense to talk about things that happened at a specific time in the past.
    Chris: Ana **went** to Los Angeles last Saturday.
    Luis: I know. She **had** a great time.
    Ana: I **had** a meeting with Mr. Arnello at 10:00. I **told** him about my job offer.
    Chris: What did he say?
    Ana: He **congratulated** me.

2. The present perfect can tell us about actions that started in the past and are still happening.
    Clara: How long **has** Chris **worked** at Silica?
    Ana: I think he**'s worked** here for a year.

    This means that Chris is working for Silica now.

3. We use the past to talk about actions that started and ended in the past.
    Clara: Mike **worked** at Silica for almost a year, too.
    Ana: Where is he now?
    Clara: I don't know.

    This means that Mike doesn't work at Silica now.

4. Here are some time expressions we use with the present perfect and the simple past:

Present perfect	Simple past
for a few hours	2 hours ago
since last year	last year
this afternoon	yesterday afternoon
this summer	last summer

5. We never use the present perfect with *ago*.
    I **met** him 3 days **ago**. (Today is Thursday. I met him Monday.)
    We don't say, *I have met him 3 days ago.*

Grammar 3: Review of Verb Tenses

1. We have learned that the simple present tense has two main uses: We use the simple present tense for facts and for things that happen again and again.
    Chris **takes** a trip every month.
    I **don't get up** at 5:00 a.m. every day.
    He **speaks** three languages.

2. We also use the simple present tense with stative verbs.
    *   Some stative verbs describe people or things.
        You **look** great.
        She**'s** a doctor.
    *   Some stative verbs describe emotions.
        Laura **loves** her children.
        She **doesn't like** dogs. She **hates** them.
    *   Some stative verbs describe ideas.
        Chris **knows** Sam.
        Chris often **forgets** names.
    *   Some stative verbs describe the senses.
        This coffee **tastes** awful.
        Emi **feels** terrible.
    *   Some stative verbs show possession.
        This apartment **belongs** to Kate.
        She **has** a nice place.

3. We use the present continuous for actions that are happening now.
    It's 2 o'clock and Emi **is sitting** in the doctor's office.
    She and the doctor **are talking**.

    We also use the present continuous to talk about things that are happening over a period of time.
    Emi **is sleeping** a lot this week.
    Dave and Rich **are working** even harder this month.

4. We sometimes use the present continuous to talk about the future.
    Kate **is eating** dinner with Ana tonight.
    Are you **going** to the party next week?

5. We use *be going to* to talk about definite plans for the future.
    Ana **is going to** stay with Sam's brother for a few days.
    Chris **isn't going to** be there.
    Are you **going to** take a present to Emi's party tonight?

    We also use *will* with the simple form of the verb to talk about future plans.
    I**'ll be** at Emi's house around 7:00 tomorrow.
    I**'ll come** visit you next year.
    He **won't study** Spanish next semester.

6. We use the simple past tense to talk about actions or events in the past.
    Ana **got** the news yesterday.
    The meeting **ended** at 10 o'clock.
    Chris **didn't finish** his work.
    The guests **left** 2 hours ago.

    We use the simple past with *when* to talk about a sequence of events.
    When I **forgot** my briefcase, I **had to** go back to the hotel.

7. We use the past continuous to show an action that is continuing in the past.

> On the plane, this little boy **was kicking** my seat.
> The mother and the little boy **were talking** all the time.
> They **weren't sleeping** during the flight.
> **Was** Sam **waiting** for you at the airport?

We use the past continuous with *when* and the simple past tense to talk about an action that was interrupted or stopped by another action.

> Kate **was calling** the office **when** Sam **arrived** at the airport.
> Kate **was running** through the airport **when** she **lost** her shoe.

8. We use the present perfect to talk about things that happened in the past. We use the present perfect when the exact time isn't important or we don't know when something happened.

> Ana **has been** to Los Angeles several times.
> **Have** you ever **been** to London?
> I've never **been** to England.
> **Has** Ana **told** Mr. Arnello about her job offer?

Audioscript

Track 1

Chris: Taxi!
Sam: Yeah.
Chris: 989 Union Street, please.
Sam: Sure. Wait, you're . . . the guy from the travel office.
Chris: Pardon me?
Sam: You came into our office last week . . . to I-Travel.
Chris: Right, I did. You look familiar, too.
Sam: Yeah, I work there part-time.
Chris: Oh, right. Now I remember you . . . So you work at I-Travel and drive a taxi?
Sam: Yeah, I have 2 part-time jobs.
Chris: Wow, 2 jobs. Sounds busy.
Sam: So . . . how was your trip?
Chris: My trip to New York? Fine.
Sam: Do you travel often?
Chris: Yeah, I have to travel for work. I work for Silica Communications. I'm in sales.

Track 2

Dispatcher: Gray Taxi.
Ana: Hi, I need a taxi.
Dispatcher: Just a second . . . OK . . . pick up . . . what's your address?
Ana: 440 Battery Street, Silica Communications.
Dispatcher: And where are you going?
Ana: 600 Bay Street, please.
Dispatcher: OK . . . and what's your name?
Ana: Ana Pedroso.
Dispatcher: Phone?
Ana: 989-0227.
Dispatcher: Ready now?
Ana: Mm-hmmm.
Dispatcher: OK, somebody'll be there in about 5, 10 minutes.
Ana: Thanks. I'll be waiting out front.
Dispatcher: OK, bye.

Track 3

Laura: Hi.
Luis: Hi.
Laura: Are you busy?
Luis: No, what's up?
Laura: I'd like you to meet someone. Luis, this is Susan Wu. She's our new project director for the Star One program. She's from Singapore.
Luis: The new project director? Glad to meet you.
Susan: Nice to meet you, too.
Laura: Luis is very talented. He's a great guy to work with.
Luis: Thanks, Laura.
Laura: Susan has a lot of experience with the company. I'm sure you'll enjoy working with her.
Luis: Yes, I'm looking forward to working with you.
Susan: Same here, Luis.
Luis: Which office will you be in?
Laura: She'll be in the office across the hall.

Luis: The corner office?
Laura: Right.
Luis: Oh. Oh, OK. When will you be moving in?
Susan: Tomorrow.
Luis: So soon? Good! Well, please let me know if you need any help with anything.
Susan: I appreciate that. Thanks.
Laura: Well, sorry for the interruption.
Luis: No problem. See you later.

Track 4

Kate: What's up at work?
Luis: Well, we got a new project director this week.
Kate: Oh really? What's he like?
Luis: She.
Kate: Well? What's she like? Is she nice?
Luis: She seems nice enough. She's young, energetic.
Kate: That sounds good. So, do you like her?
Luis: I don't know yet. Tomorrow I've got my first meeting with her.
Kate: Oh?
Luis: I have to update her on the Star One project. I'm a little nervous.
Kate: Oh, don't be. I'm sure it'll be fine.

Track 5

Emi: Hi, Dave.
Dave: Oh, hi, Emi. What can I get for you?
Emi: I'd like a tuna fish sandwich.
Dave: For here or to go?
Emi: For here.
Dave: Sure. What kind of bread would you like?
Emi: Bread? Whole wheat, I guess.
Dave: Sorry, we don't have any whole wheat. How about white or rye?
Emi: White is fine.
Dave: Would you like a slice of tomato or lettuce on it?
Emi: Um. Tomato or lettuce? Just lettuce, no tomato.
Dave: Would you like mustard or mayo?
Emi: Dave, look, I don't really care. Just give me a tuna fish sandwich!
Dave: Sure. One tuna fish sandwich. Coming right up! . . . Anything to drink with that?
Emi: Maybe some iced tea.
Dave: With ice?
Emi: Of course!
Dave: Sure. Large, medium, or small?
Emi: Small.
Dave: Regular or decaf?
Emi: Regular or decaf? You have decaf tea?
Dave: Emi, there's always a choice, didn't you know that?
Emi: OK, Dave. Regular.
Dave: With sugar or sweetener?
Emi: Dave, cut it out! Why are there so many choices?

Track 6

Dave: Rock Café. Can I help you?
Customer: Do you do take-out orders?
Dave: Sure. What would you like?

Customer: I'd like 3 sandwiches: 2 ham and 1 tuna.
Dave: What kind of bread?
Customer: Whole wheat for the ham sandwiches.
Dave: With cheese?
Customer: Yeah, both with everything on them.
Dave: Mustard, mayo, pickles?
Customer: Yeah, with everything.
Dave: And the tuna?
Customer: Tuna on white bread.
Dave: Anything on that?
Customer: Just lettuce.
Dave: Anything else?
Customer: Yeah, could you throw in 3 bags of potato chips?
Dave: OK. Something to drink?
Customer: I guess . . . 3 bottles of something . . . like . . . mineral water. Yeah, mineral water.
Dave: OK, you got it. It'll be ready in about 15 minutes. Your name?

Unit A.4

Track 7

Ana: Hi, Chris. How was your weekend?
Chris: Boring. I was at home all weekend. How about you?
Ana: You know me. I'm never home on weekends.
Chris: Where were you?
Ana: I was in L.A. on Saturday and Sunday.
Chris: Where?
Ana: Los Angeles.
Chris: Oh, wow! What did you do?
Ana: Well, we did a bunch of tourist stuff—shopping, beach, movie studios.
Chris: Ah. Did you have a good time?
Ana: Oh, yeah, it was great. But I spent *way* too much money.
Chris: Who . . . who did you go with?
Ana: Emi and Sam.
Chris: Oh. How did you get there?
Ana: We flew.
Chris: Wasn't that expensive?
Ana: No, it was really cheap. Sam had these great discount coupons.
Chris: Where did you guys stay?
Ana: Oh, Sam has a brother in L.A. We stayed at his place.
Chris: Ah. Wasn't that . . . crowded?
Ana: No, it was a lot of fun. You know, Chris, you ought to come with us next time.
Chris: Hmm. Maybe.

Track 8

Computer voice: Thank you for calling U.S. Rail. For schedules, press 1 . . .

For schedules from San Francisco, press 1, for schedules from . . .

For schedules from San Francisco, east, press 1; for schedules north, press 2; for schedules south, press 3.

We have trains from San Francisco to San Diego, every day, at 6:45, 8:45, and 11:00 a.m. and at 2:15, 5:30, 7:45, and 11:15 p.m. All trains stop at San Jose, Salinas, San Luis Obispo, Santa Barbara, Los Angeles, and San Diego.

For arrival times, press 1. For fares, press 2. To repeat . . .

For San Jose, press 1; for Salinas, press 2; for San Luis Obispo, press 3; for Santa Barbara, press 4; for Los Angeles, press 5 . . .

One-way fares from San Francisco to Los Angeles are $40. Round-trip fares from San Francisco to Los Angeles are $65. To reserve a ticket, press 1 . . .

Unit A.5

Track 9

Laura: Hi, Frankie. What are you doing?
Frank: Homework.
Laura: Need any help?
Frank: Uh, yeah. Can you show me how to use this math program?
Laura: Sure . . . just type the numbers in column 1 . . .
Frank: OK. Do I have to hit "return"?
Laura: Right. You have to hit "return" after each number. OK, oops . . . careful . . . do it carefully. Good!
Frank: Cool. OK, now how do I add them?
Laura: Next, you need to highlight the numbers . . . and now you have to click on "add."
Frank: And that's the answer?
Laura: That's it. Pretty cool, huh?
Frank: Wow. That's easy. You don't have to think.
Laura: Yeah, computers are great . . . but, Frankie, you have to learn how to add numbers the *real* way.
Frank: The real way? This *is* the real way.
Laura: Well, you know what I mean. You have to learn how to add without a computer.
Frank: Why do I have to learn that?
Laura: That's a good question. It's important.
Frank: But why?
Laura: Believe it or not, Frankie, you won't have a computer with you when you need to add something.
Frank: Why not?

Track 10

Kevin: Eversoft Help Desk. This is Kevin. Which software are you calling about?
Customer: Oh, it's this . . . Super Math program . . .
Kevin: Super Math . . . How can I help you?
Customer: Well, I'm trying to help my son with his homework.
Kevin: What do you have to do?
Customer: We need to add a list of numbers.
Kevin: OK, you want to add a list of numbers . . .
Customer: Right.
Kevin: All you have to do is enter the data and perform the function.
Customer: Well, yes, but . . . that's why I'm calling . . . where do we enter the data?
Kevin: Oh . . . Type the numbers in column 1. Do you see column 1?
Customer: Yep.
Kevin: Type one number, then press "return," then type the next number, etcetera.
Customer: Mm-hmmm . . . OK.
Kevin: Then you highlight all the numbers and click on the "add" sign.
Customer: Click on the what?
Kevin: On the "add" sign. Do you see it?
Customer: No. Where is it?
Kevin: On the top menu bar.
Customer: Oh, on the top! Right. Got it.
Kevin: Great. Anything else?
Customer: No, that's it. Thanks.
Kevin: No problem. Thank you for calling Eversoft.

Unit B.1

Track 11

Emi: What kind of medication do I need?
Doctor: You have a sinus infection, so I'm giving you some Azithromycin.
Emi: Azithro-*what?* What's that?
Doctor: It's an antibiotic. You need to take it for 5 days.
Emi: What do I do with this?
Doctor: That's the prescription. Take it to the pharmacy, and they'll fill it for you.
Emi: Thank you.
Doctor: Oh, and I know you're busy, but you need to take it easy for a few days, OK?
Emi: I know. I definitely need some rest.
Doctor: OK. Bye-bye.
Emi: Bye.

Track 12

Nurse: Hello. This is Elizabeth. May I help you?
Ana: I'm feeling terrible. I'd like to make an appointment to see the doctor.
Nurse: What are your symptoms?
Ana: Ohhh . . . a headache . . . and a terrible sore throat.
Nurse: Do you have a fever?
Ana: Yes.
Nurse: How long have you had these symptoms?
Ana: About 2 or 3 days . . . since Saturday.
Nurse: Any cough?
Ana: No cough, but my throat is killing me. Can I come in to see the doctor? I think I have strep throat or something.
Nurse: Let me see what I can do . . . Let's see, I can fit you in Friday the 12th at 3:45 p.m. . . .
Ana: The 12th? Isn't there anything sooner?
Nurse: I'll see what I can do. Just a moment. How about this afternoon at 2:30, with Dr. Lee?
Ana: That's perfect. Thank you.

Unit B.2

Track 13

Luis: Hello. Luis Mendez.
Laura: Luis, it's Laura. Where are you?
Luis: What do you mean—where am I? I'm here. I'm in the office. You're talking to me.
Laura: But we have a meeting with Lucid Systems, at 1 o'clock!
Luis: At 1? Oh, man! How do I get to Lucid?
Laura: It's on Ashby, 3121 Ashby, near Telegraph Avenue. Take College Avenue to Ashby, and turn right.
Luis: Got it.
Laura: Hurry!
Luis: I'm on my way.
Laura: Oh, Luis?
Luis: Yeah?
Laura: Be sure to bring the Lucid file.
Luis: Where is it?
Laura: I put it on your desk this morning.
Luis: You did?
Laura: Remember? I put it next to your computer.
Luis: Oh, right. Yeah, here it is.
Laura: And, Luis, please hurry. I need to talk to you about . . .
Luis: OK, we'll talk about it when I get there. Bye.

Track 14

Computer voice: Thank you for calling the Civic Arena. The Civic Arena is located at 111 First Street in downtown San Jose. For directions, please press 1.

If you're coming from San Francisco, take Highway 101 to Highway 880 North, go 1 mile to First Street, exit at First Street, and turn right. The Civic Arena is at the corner of First Street and Montgomery Street.

Unit B.3

Track 15

Emi: I just want to thank everyone for coming . . . this is a really special day for me. I'm going back to Japan next week, but I'll always remember my fabulous time here . . . and I will miss all of you. Someday you'll all have to come visit me in Japan. So thanks, everybody, for being such great friends . . . I think I'm going to cry.

Track 16

Emi's voicemail: Hi, this is Emi. You've reached my cell phone. I can't take your call right now. Please leave a message and I'll call you back later. Bye.
Jin: Hi, Emi. This is Jin. I'm calling from Seattle. I'm so sorry I can't be at your farewell party tonight. I won't be back until Monday. I just want to say "Good luck." If I don't see you before you go, I'm sure I'll see you sometime soon. I mean, I hope so! Who knows? Maybe I'll have a chance to visit you in Japan some day. Bye!

Unit B.4

Track 17

Laura: Hi, guys. Oh good, you got the groceries.
Frank: Yeah! We got a lot of good stuff.
Laura: Mmm . . . did you pick up some lettuce?
Paul: Oh, lettuce. Darn! I forgot to get that.
Laura: Oh. Did you remember to buy some tomatoes?
Paul: Tomatoes? Shoot! I didn't know we needed tomatoes.
Frank: But look, Mom, we got a big box of Crunch-O's cereal, a 6-pack of Orange Plus, 3 bags of chips, and 2 cartons of ice cream.
Maggie: Hey, Chocolate Crunch . . . excellent choice!
Laura: Good work, guys.

Track 18

Computer voice: Hello, Mr. Chen. How are you today? Are you ready to order? Please click yes if . . . Please enter your shopping list now . . . Thank you, Mr. Chen. Your order is:

15 pounds of French roast coffee
8 loaves of whole wheat bread
7 heads of lettuce
3 large cans of tuna fish
2 cartons of eggs
20 tomatoes
1 large jar of mayonnaise
2 cases of orange juice

Is that all for today? Thank you. Your order will be shipped immediately. It will arrive by 11 a.m. tomorrow. Your account will be charged $172.43. Thank you.

Unit B.5

Track 19

Maggie: Hi, it's Maggie. Maggie Arnello. From 3rd-period math.
Brian: Hey, what's up?
Maggie: Um . . . I was wondering . . . if you . . . had a date for the dance on Friday?
Brian: No.
Maggie: Well, I was wondering if you . . . Do you want to go to the dance with me? We could just go as friends, we could . . .
Brian: You want to go to the dance with me?
Maggie: Yeah . . .
Brian: Cool. But do we have to dance?
Maggie: Well, no . . . but it is a dance . . .
Brian: Oh . . . but I don't have to dress up, do I?
Maggie: No, you don't have to dress up. Well, maybe you can pick me up or something?
Brian: Sure. What time?
Maggie: Well, the dance starts at 8:00, so maybe, like, 7:30?
Brian: Yeah, cool.
Maggie: OK, great, see you later?
Brian: Later.

Track 20

Dr. Fournier: Good morning, West Park students. This is Dr. Fournier. I want to remind everyone that tonight is the night of the spring dance, and I'd like to review the guidelines so that there are *no* misunderstandings, like last year. This year, the spring dance is a *non*-smoking event. There will be *no* smoking anywhere in the gymnasium, in the parking lot, or anywhere on the school grounds. This year, there will be *no* containers allowed in the gymnasium . . . no cans, no bottles, no plastic containers of any kind. And finally, the dance will end promptly at 11 p.m. The parking lot gates will be locked at 11:15 p.m. *All* cars must be out of the parking lot by 11:15. Thank you for your cooperation. Please have a wonderful time!

Unit C.1

Track 21

Ana: Kate! Welcome back!
Kate: Thanks.
Ana: You look tired.
Kate: Ahhh . . . I'm exhausted . . .
Ana: What happened?
Kate: What didn't happen?! First, I left my hotel in New York at 6:00 this morning. But I forgot my briefcase, so I had to go back and get it.
Ana: Oh, Kate . . .
Kate: And then I missed my flight . . .
Ana: Ohhh . . .
Kate: So I had to wait 2 hours for the next flight. It was so frustrating!
Ana: I bet.
Kate: And I sat next to this lady who talked and talked, and this little kid kept kicking my seat! I almost lost my mind!
Ana: Oh, no! That's terrible. Where's your suitcase?
Kate: Well, when I arrived, my bag wasn't at the baggage claim!
Ana: That's so annoying, I can't believe it! Well, at least *you* made it! . . . By the way, what were you doing in New York?
Kate: I was there on business. Our head office is in New York, and I was at a national meeting.
Ana: Oh, I see. Did that go well?

Kate: It was great. Lots of interesting presentations. So much new stuff. I am sooo brain-dead now!
Ana: Well, get some rest, and I hope they find your suitcase.
Kate: Thanks, Ana.

Track 22

Kate: Hello. . . . Yes, this is Kate Taylor. . . . Yes, I reported the lost bag . . . That's right, Flight 129 out of New York . . . JFK . . . it's a black Luggage-Pro . . . Yes, it has my name on it . . . Great, you found it! . . . It's here? . . . yes, I *do* need it tonight. . . . Thank you. . . . The address . . . is 3864 Lake Street. . . . Right . . . 3864 Lake Street, off of Clement Street. . . . That's right . . . apartment 201. . . . How soon will the driver be here? OK, good! Yes, thank you. Bye.

Unit C.2

Track 23

Landlady: It has a lovely view of the ocean.
Kate: That's a view of the ocean?
Landlady: And this is the garden!
Kate: This is the garden? . . .
Landlady: And here is the kitchen . . . fully equipped with all the modern conveniences!
Kate: Ah, well, thanks for showing the place to me. I will definitely give this some consideration . . .
Landlady: Well, I would encourage you to act quickly. This beautiful place won't last long.

Track 24

Computer voice: Thank you for calling Rent Master. Here are our new rental listings for Monday . . . For monthly rents under one thousand dollars, press 1 . . . For monthly rents between one thousand and fifteen hundred dollars, press 2.

A studio apartment; 400 Lake Street, Oakland; a nice view of Lake Merritt; a lovely, classic building; unfurnished; utilities included; twelve hundred dollars.

A 1-bedroom condominium; furnished; 2020 University Avenue, Berkeley; easy access to buses and subway; twelve fifty.

A 2-bedroom house; 505 Clement Street, San Francisco; an old neighborhood with wide-open spaces; nice garden; thirteen ninety.

A 1-bedroom apartment; unfurnished; 101 Spear Street, San Francisco; a new neighborhood with great views of the bay, fourteen fifty.

To repeat these listings, press 1 . . .

Unit C.3

Track 25

Kate: Luis, where are you from?
Luis: San Francisco—you know that!
Kate: No, no. I mean, where is your family from?
Luis: Oh, my parents are from Mexico.
Kate: But where in Mexico?
Luis: Colima.
Kate: Calina?
Luis: That's close.
Kate: Where is that?
Luis: It's in western Mexico.
Kate: Is it close to Mexico City?
Luis: Not far. Here, I'll show you. It's somewhere around here . . . here.

Kate: Oh, Colima! What's it like there?

Luis: It's near the ocean and the mountains. I think it's the most beautiful place on Earth. . . . How about you? Where's your family from?

Kate: Well, I was born in California. My father moved here from Georgia in the 1950s . . .

Luis: Oh?

Kate: And my mother moved here from Texas in the 1960s.

Luis: Uh-huh.

Kate: They met and got married . . . and here I am!

Luis: Wow! Everyone's got a story, huh?

Track 26

Tour guide: Good morning everyone. Thank you for joining our tour today. We're now leaving Union Square . . . this square officially became a public park in 1861 . . . and is a famous place for public gatherings . . . Of course, around Union Square are all of San Francisco's major shops and department stores . . . We're now heading up Powell Street and up here, on the top of Nob Hill, you can see the luxurious Fairmont Hotel . . . the place where presidents and kings stay when they're in San Francisco . . . Across from the Fairmont Hotel is the majestic Grace Cathedral . . . it was built in 1928 and was modeled after Notre Dame Cathedral in Paris . . . And if you look straight ahead, down the hill, you can see a lovely view of the San Francisco Bay, and the Golden Gate Bridge off in the distance . . .

Unit C.4

Track 27

Sam: What's this little dish?

Emi: That's the *sashimishoyuzara*.

Sam: The what?

Emi: It's a dish that you use for the soy sauce.

Sam: Oh. And this is the soy sauce, isn't it?

Emi: Mm-hmmm.

Sam: And what's this green stuff?

Emi: It's called *wasabi*.

Sam: *Wasabi*?

Emi: Mm-hmmm. It's like horseradish. It's a spice that you mix with the soy sauce.

Sam: I'll try it.

Emi: Careful. It's very spicy.

Sam: Good. I love spicy food.

Emi: Wait, wait, wait!

Sam: Wow, that is spicy!

Emi: Here, drink some water . . . You OK?

Sam: Whew! Yeah, I'm OK. Next time, I won't eat the whole thing.

Emi: Sam, you're supposed to *mix* it with the soy sauce!

Track 28

Luis: Hello.

Kate: Hi, Luis. This is Kate. I'm having some friends over for dinner, and I'd like to make that "sev-eech" dish you told me about.

Luis: Oh, ceviche?

Kate: Yeah. Can you tell me how to make it?

Luis: Oh, sure . . . Let's see . . . I'll teach you an easy way to make it . . . It's not the traditional way . . . but it's easier. Just get some fish, like sea bass . . .

Kate: OK . . .

Luis: And marinate it in olive oil and lime juice . . .

Kate: Mm-hmmm.

Luis: And then chop up some tomato and onion . . .

Kate: Right . . .

Luis: And mix it all together.

Kate: That's it?

Luis: Well, basically . . . I mean, I have my own secret sauce . . .

Kate: And . . . ?

Luis: But it's a secret . . . I don't tell anybody!

Unit C.5

Track 29

Ana: Have you heard?

Chris: Heard what?

Ana: I got a job offer from Media View.

Chris: Really? From Media View. Where are they?

Ana: London!

Chris: Wow, that's great. Have you ever been to London?

Ana: No, I've never been to England, period!

Chris: Well, what are you going to do?

Ana: I think you know . . .

Ana and Chris: You gotta do what you gotta do!

Chris: So you're going to take it?

Ana: Yeah, I just can't pass this up.

Chris: Have you told Mr. Arnello?

Ana: Yep, I told him this morning, and he totally understood.

Chris: Well, what are you going to do there?

Ana: I'm going to be assistant art director. It's a big step up for me.

Chris: Wow, great! When do you start?

Ana: Next month. I can't wait. London!

Chris: Well, Ana, I'm really happy for you. We're going to miss you around here!

Track 30

Receptionist: Good afternoon, Media View.

Ana: Hello . . . This is Ana Pedroso. Could I speak with Andrew Jones please?

Receptionist: I'll put you through.

Mr. Jones: Hello. This is Andrew Jones.

Ana: Hello, Mr. Jones. This is Ana Pedroso.

Mr. Jones: Oh, Ana, how are you?

Ana: Good. Very good.

Mr. Jones: Have you thought about the job offer?

Ana: Yes, I have . . . and I've decided to accept the offer.

Mr. Jones: That's wonderful! I'm very pleased to hear that.

Ana: Yes, I've thought it over carefully, and I'm sure it's the right thing to do.

Mr. Jones: Well, that's excellent. Let me connect you with our human resources person, and we'll get this all sorted out for you.

Ana: Thank you, Mr. Jones.

Mr. Jones: Thank you, Ana. I'm looking forward to working with you.

Answer Key

Unit A.1

Listening

A. 2. the guy from the travel office
3. You came into our office last week.
4. You look familiar, too.
5. I work there part-time.
6. Two jobs. Sounds busy.
7. How was your trip?
8. Do you travel often?
9. I have to travel for work.
10. I'm in sales.

B. 1. 440 Battery Street
2. 600 Bay Street
3. In 5 to 10 minutes
4. In front of the building

Vocabulary

2. musician
3. sales representative (sales rep)
4. cashier
5. taxi driver
6. travel agent
7. office worker
8. instructor
9. intern
10. designer
11. small business owner
12. programmer

Grammar 1

2. They're
3. Are you; I'm; I'm an
4. Are you; is
5. We're
6. He's an

Grammar 2

3. Do Kate and Sam work at I-Travel?
4. Does Ana work
5. Yes, he speaks Spanish.
6. Does Chris work at I-Travel (*or* Globe Technologies)?
7. Do Kate and Sam speak French?
8. Does Sam work at Gray Taxi? (*or* Does Sam drive a taxi?)

Grammar 3

1. No, they aren't. / No, they're not.
2. Yes, they do.
3. Yes, they are.
4. No, she's not. / No, she isn't.
5. No, he doesn't.
6. No, they don't.
7. Yes, they are.
8. Yes, they do.
9. Yes, he is.

Unit A.2

Listening

A. **Laura:** Hi.
Luis: Hi.
Laura: Are you busy?
Luis: No, what's up?
Laura: I'd like you to meet someone. Luis, this is Susan Wu. She's our new project <u>director</u> for the Star One program. She's from <u>Singapore</u>.
Luis: The new project director? Glad to meet you.
Susan: Nice to meet you, too.
Laura: Luis is very <u>talented</u>; he's <u>a great</u> guy to work with.
Luis: Thanks, Laura.
Laura: Susan has a lot of experience with the company. I'm sure you'll enjoy working with her.
Luis: Yes, I'm looking forward to working <u>with</u> you.
Susan: Same here, Luis.
Luis: Which <u>office</u> will you be in?
Laura: She'll be in the office across the hall.
Luis: The <u>corner</u> office?
Laura: Right.
Luis: Oh. Oh, OK. When will you be moving in?
Susan: <u>Tomorrow</u>.
Luis: So soon? Good! Well, please let me know if you need <u>any help with</u> anything.
Susan: I appreciate that. Thanks.
Laura: Well, sorry for the interruption.
Luis: <u>No problem</u>. See you later.

BONUS
Luis feels jealous because the corner office is better than his office. He also feels nervous about having a new boss.

B. 1. He's a little nervous because he has a meeting with his new boss tomorrow.
2. Don't be nervous. It will be fine.

Vocabulary

117

Grammar 1

A. **2.** *adj:* small; big; tiny   *qual:* kind of; not very; very
  3. *adj:* nice; terrible; rainy; cold   *qual:* so
  4. *adj:* mean; true; friendly   *qual:* really; very
  5. *adj:* hot; cold; another   *qual:* very; too

B. Sample sentences:
  1. My dog, Rex, is sort of ugly. He's not so cute.
  2. My house is kind of old. It's not very new.
  3. My girlfriend, Keiko, is very smart. She isn't usually sad.

Grammar 2

Sample answers:
Su-Lin <u>is about 28 years old</u>.
She <u>has long black hair</u>.
She <u>is from China</u>.
She <u>is a reporter</u> at Veritas News Agency.

Darius <u>is 25 years old</u>.
He <u>has straight brown hair</u>.
He <u>is Brazilian</u>.
He <u>is a programmer</u> at AllSoft Computers.

Sarah and Andrea <u>are 16 years old</u>.
They <u>are American</u>.
They <u>are students</u> at Washington High School.

Grammar 3

  2. What's that?
  3. Where is she?
  4. What time is it?
  5. What do you want?
  6. Who wants it?

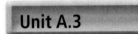

Unit A.3

Listening

A. **2.** what kind of bread
  3. a slice of tomato
  4. no tomato
  5. mustard or mayo
  6. one tuna fish sandwich
  7. some iced tea
  8. large, medium, or small
  9. regular or decaf
  10. with sugar or sweetener
  11. Why are there so many choices?

B. 3 sandwiches: 2 ham/1 tuna
Ham sandwiches on whole wheat bread, with everything (cheese, mustard, mayo, pickles)
Tuna sandwich on white bread, with lettuce
3 bags of potato chips
3 bottles of mineral water

Vocabulary

1. meals   **3.** menu   **5.** choose
2. snack   **4.** order   **6.** take-out food

BONUS   Sample answers:
  a can of soda   a loaf of bread
  a carton of orange juice   a bottle of mineral water
  a few hamburgers   a slice of pizza
  a glass of milk   a stick of butter
  a jar of honey   a cup of coffee

Grammar 1

A. **1.** ∅; ∅   **3.** ∅; an   **5.** ∅; a
  2. ∅; a   **4.** ∅; a   **6.** ∅; an; ∅

B.

Count	Non-count	
chair	knowledge	meat
apple	advice	milk
dollar	baggage	money
idea	bread	music
jar	cheese	oil
sandwich	education	pepper
ticket	English	salt
woman	experience	time
	fun	weather
	love	work

Grammar 2

A. Sample sentences:
  2. I want some coffee, but I don't want any tea.
  3. I need a new notebook, but I don't need any pens.
  4. I'll buy some juice, but I won't buy any soda.
  5. I know some French, but I don't know any Spanish.
  6. There are some Brazilian students in my class, but there aren't any Japanese students.
  7. There's some butter in my refrigerator, but there isn't any milk.

B. Sample answers:
  1. No, I don't have any.   **3.** Yes, there are some.
  2. Yes, I want some.   **4.** Yes, I have some.

Grammar 3

  2. Yes, I'd love a glass of iced tea.
  3. There are only a few left.
  4. Just a little.
  5. How many employees do you have?

Unit A.4

Listening

A. **2.** Los Angeles   **6.** some friends
     3. tourist   **7.** flew
     4. great   **8.** stayed
     5. too much   **9.** invited

B. **1.** From San Francisco to Los Angeles
     2. One-way: $40   Round-trip: $65

Vocabulary

A. **2.** reserve; b   **4.** schedule; f   **6.** cancel; e
     3. check in; c   **5.** fare; a

B. **2.** fare   **4.** cancel   **6.** tourist
     3. reserve   **5.** check in

Grammar 1

B. **2.** Yes, she was.
     3. Yes, he was.
     4. Yes, he was.
     5. Yes, they were.
     6. No, they weren't. They were at home eating dinner.
     7. Yes, he was.
     8. No, he wasn't. He was at the airport, at the gym, at Tony's office, at home, and at a party.
     9. No, she wasn't. She was there on Friday morning.
    10. No, they weren't. Laura was there, but Paul wasn't there.

Grammar 2

     1. stayed; watched
     2. were; weren't; was
     3. arrived; missed
     4. was; was; loved; did you stay, stayed

BONUS   Sample answers:
     1. Was Laura in a meeting at 9:30?
     2. Where was Paul at 2:30?
     3. Where were Laura and Paul at the gym together?

Grammar 3

A. **2.** found   **3.** met   **4.** came

B. **2.** broke   **7.** found   **12.** practiced
     3. caught   **8.** got   **13.** saw
     4. changed   **9.** gave   **14.** wanted
     5. came   **10.** went
     6. enjoyed   **11.** met

C. Sample sentences:
     1. I practiced piano last night.
     2. Yesterday I met a new student, Paulo.
     3. I practiced irregular verbs in my last English class.
     4. I saw a movie last Saturday.
     5. When I was a child, I wanted to be a movie star.

Unit A.5

Listening

A. **2.** a   **4.** b   **6.** d   **8.** c   **10.** g
     3. i   **5.** e   **7.** j   **9.** f

B. **1.** She can't use the   **4.** Yes.
        Super Math program.   **5.** Yes.
     2. Frustrated.   **6.** Yes.
     3. Calm.

Vocabulary

     1. log on   **3.** insert   **5.** download
     2. delete   **4.** browse   **6.** freeze

Grammar 1

A. **2.** Emi can speak English and Japanese. She can't speak Spanish.
     3. Kate can speak English and French. She can't speak Spanish.
     5. Luis should hang out more with his friends. He shouldn't watch so much television.
     6. Paul should get more exercise. He shouldn't eat so many fatty foods.
     8. Frankie has to do some housework every day. He doesn't have to do homework on the weekends.
     9. Maggie has to do the grocery shopping for her family sometimes. She doesn't have to cook meals for her family.

B. Sample sentences:
     1. I can sing pretty well.
     2. I shouldn't stay out so late on Saturday night.
     3. I can't play piano very well, but I'm learning!
     4. I don't have to study English every day, but I usually do.
     5. I should call my parents more often.
     6. My teacher has to work very hard. She has so many students.

Grammar 2

     2. Raise   **7.** stand   **12.** put/place
     3. make   **8.** Do   **13.** Go
     4. Do   **9.** sit   **14.** Don't hurry
     5. change   **10.** Be   **15.** Breathe
     6. touch   **11.** Place/Put   **16.** Smile

Grammar 3

     3. adverb   **8.** adjective   **13.** adverb
     4. adjective   **9.** adverb   **14.** adjective
     5. adverb   **10.** adverb   **15.** adverb
     6. adverb   **11.** adjective
     7. adverb   **12.** adjective

BONUS   Sample answers:
     1. I slept deeply last night.
     2. I did my homework carefully.
     3. I got to school early today.

Unit B.1

Listening

A.
2. have	5. do I do	8. know
3. I'm giving	6. Take	9. need
4. need	7. 'll fill	10. need

B.
1. She has a headache, a terrible sore throat, and a fever.
2. See the doctor
3. Dr. Lee
4. this afternoon at 2:30

Vocabulary

1. infection	4. injury	7. check up
2. prescription	5. headache	8. waiting room
3. fever	6. nauseous	

BONUS Sample answers:
Health problems: earache, sprained ankle
Medications: eye drops, ointment
Health professionals: surgeon, ambulance driver

Grammar 1

B.
2. is getting; Rule 4	5. need; Rule 2
3. hate; Rule 2	6. 's talking; Rule 3
4. get up; Rule 1	

BONUS: Sample answers:
Rule 1: I take the subway to work every day.
Rule 2: I don't like taking the subway.
Rule 3: I'm looking out the window.
Rule 4: I'm getting sleepy.

Grammar 2

B.
2. remember; forget	7. prefer
3. suppose/believe	8. Do you realize
4. need/want	9. doesn't contain
5. don't have/feel like	10. don't own/wish
6. matter	

Grammar 3

A.
1. Did you say "fever"?
2. What do you call this in English?
3. What do you mean by "every other day"?
4. What did you say?
5. What does this sign mean?

B. a. 4   b. 5   c. 1   d. 2   e. 3

Unit B.2

Listening

A.
1. in	4. at	7. on	10. on
2. to	5. At	8. near	11. next to
3. with	6. to	9. to	12. about

B. 101; 880; 1 mile; exit; right; corner

Vocabulary

A.
1. location	3. blocks	5. direction
2. exit	4. Take a right	6. intersection

B. Crossed-out items:
2. a distance	5. get into the first car
3. this destination	6. do it correctly
4. a small building	

Grammar 1

Sample answers:
1. I'm in my room.
2. No, nobody is next to me.
3. The window is in front of me.
4. There's a computer and some books on my desk. The computer is in front of the lamp. The books are near the computer.
5. Yes, I'm sitting between a wall and a bookcase.
6. Yes, I'm sitting on a chair.
7. My file cabinets are behind me.
8. My office is at 559 Pacific Avenue.
9. Monument Park is the most famous place in this city. It's near the river.

Grammar 2

1. the post office/the hospital
2. Wired Café
3. Scoops Restaurant/bank
4. Star Hotel
5. Wired Café
6. the bank/the football stadium

Grammar 3

B. Sample answers:
1. Ouch.	4. Oops.	7. Yuck.
2. Mmm.	5. Whew!	8. Cool.
3. Hurray!	6. Uh-oh.	

BONUS Sample answers:
1. You win tickets to a concert by your favorite band.
2. You are drinking lemonade on a hot day.
3. You get a job you really want.
4. Your friend can't meet you for dinner.

Unit B.3

Listening

A.
1. thank	4. remember	7. great
2. special	5. will miss	8. cry
3. going	6. visit	

B.
1. Jin
2. He's in Seattle.
3. luck; I'll see you again

Vocabulary

B.
2. farewell
3. New Year's Eve
4. graduation
5. birthday
6. end-of-semester
7. costume
8. anniversary

Grammar 1

A.
2. He'll give me a ride./He's going to give me a ride
3. 're going to see a movie
4. are you going to study
5. What are you going to do
6. I won't be/I'm not going to be
7. Why are you going to go

B. Sample answers:
1. Yes, I am. OR No, I'm not.
2. Yes, I will. OR No, I won't.
3. At home.
4. I'll cook dinner. OR I'm going to cook dinner.
5. Yes, we are. OR No, we're not.

Grammar 2

B. Sample answers:

Time	will/going to	might/may
1. Tonight	I'm going to do homework.	I might rent a video.
2. This weekend	I'm going to hang out with friends.	I may see a movie.
3. Tomorrow morning	I'm going to go to school.	I might have coffee at Starbucks.
4. Next month	I will visit my friend in New York.	I may buy a new computer.
5. About 5 years from now	I will live in Los Angeles.	I might get married.

Grammar 3

1. birthday
2. anniversary
3. Congratulations
4. That's great; happy
5. sorry
6. care

Unit B.4

Listening

A.
1. groceries
2. stuff
3. lettuce
4. tomatoes
5. tomatoes
6. box
7. cereal
8. six-pack
9. bags
10. cartons

BONUS Sample answers:
I like to buy fruit and coffee cake.

B. coffee, whole wheat bread, lettuce, tuna fish, eggs, tomatoes, mayonnaise, orange juice
The items will arrive by 11 a.m. tomorrow.
The total charge is $172.43.

Vocabulary

A.
1. c
2. f
3. d
4. e
5. a
6. b
7. g
8. k
9. j
10. i
11. h

B.

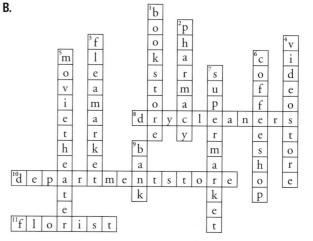

Grammar 1

A.

make	do
a cake	business
a decision	the cooking
a list	the dishes
a mistake	math
a suggestion	your homework
an effort	your best
friends	some work
your bed	the housework

B.
1. do
2. make
3. do

Grammar 2

B.
1. I'm going to the supermarket to get some groceries.
2. Wow, it's getting late.
3. I'm getting tired.
4. It's getting cold.
5. Her English is getting better.
6. My cold isn't getting better.
7. We'd better get out of here.
8. It's time to get on the train.

Grammar 3

2. a, the
3. ∅; The/∅
4. the
5. ∅
6. the, the

Unit B.5

Listening

A.
1. dance
2. Friday
3. to go
4. want to
5. have to dance
6. don't have to
7. you can
8. starts

B. Rule 1: smoking   Rule 3: parking lot
Rule 2: containers

Vocabulary

1. have a date
2. propose
3. get along
4. single
5. engaged
6. get dressed up

Grammar 1

A.

Verb + -gerund (*-ing*)	Verb + infinitive (*to*)	Verb + gerund or infinitive
enjoy	decide	forget
feel like	learn	hate
keep	need	like
miss	plan	love
practice	promise	prefer
Bonus:	want	*Bonus:*
avoid	would like	stop
spend time		try
	Bonus:	
	agree	
	expect	
	hope	

B. Sample answers:
1. Does Emi miss seeing her family
2. Why did you decide to quit your job
3. I don't enjoy going to parties in the dormitory.
4. Kate loves speaking Spanish at work.
5. Chris promised to call me last night, but he didn't.

Grammar 2

Sample answers:
2. You shouldn't wait for him to call you./I think you should call him and talk about it.
3. Let's take a gift./Why don't we take something to drink?
4. Try taking a nap first./Maybe you could do it tomorrow morning.
5. Try drinking some green tea./I don't think you should drink coffee.
6. Maybe you could tell her./Why don't you write her a note?

Grammar 3

A.
1. is too strong./isn't strong enough.
2. It's too expensive.
3. he isn't good enough.
4. I'm too busy (to go out for lunch).

B.
1. Is The Patio Café too expensive?
2. Is this soup hot enough?

Unit C.1

Listening

A.
1. trip
2. hotel
3. briefcase
4. missed
5. wait
6. lady
7. kid
8. lost
9. arrived
10. baggage
11. meeting
12. presentations

B.
1. Kate Taylor
2. lost bag (suitcase)
3. W129 (out of New York, JFK airport)
4. suitcase was (is) it
5. name on it
6. tonight

Vocabulary

A.
1. reservation
2. connection
3. suitcase
4. documents
5. check, luggage
6. overbooked
7. agent
8. jet-lagged
9. delayed
10. baggage claim area

B. Airline agent: 2, 3, 4, 5, 6, 7, 9, 10
Passenger: 1, 8

Grammar 1

A.
1. was talking
2. were playing
3. was cooking
4. was leaving
5. were listening
6. was studying
7. were painting
8. wasn't doing; was relaxing
9. wasn't watching; was working
10. was driving

BONUS Sample answer:
At 8:15 last night, I was studying English.

B.
1. were you playing
2. were you waiting
3. were you doing
4. was she going
5. was he listening
6. Were you watching

Grammar 2

2. A—waiting
3. C—met
4. B—missed
5. C—was listening

Grammar 3

1. First; Then
2. First; After
3. After; When

BONUS Sample answer:
You: It was great. First I went to a really interesting class. Then I had a nice dinner with some friends.

Unit C.2

Listening

A.
1. lovely
2. fully
3. modern
4. definitely
5. quickly
6. beautiful
7. long

BONUS
Kate doesn't believe the landlady's descriptions. Her intonation of "That's a view of the ocean?" and "This is the garden?" are sarcastic—they show she doesn't believe the landlady.

B.

	Rent	Type	Furnished?	Special features
400 Lake St.	$1,200	Studio	No	View of lake, classic building, utilities included
2020 University Ave.	$1,250	1-bedroom apt.	Yes	Easy access to buses and subway
505 Clement St.	$1,390	2-bedroom house	No information	Nice garden, old neighborhood
101 Spear St.	$1,450	1-bedroom apt.	No	New neighborhood, great views

Vocabulary

1. neighborhood
2. rent
3. convenient
4. view
5. utilities
6. lease
7. furnished
8. spacious

Grammar 1

2. Luis is much/a lot busier than Chris.
3. Chris's rent is much more expensive/higher than Luis's rent.
4. Chris's apartment is much more spacious/bigger than Luis's apartment.

Grammar 2

	Gilberto	Marta	Toshi	Helena
Age	23	21	31	18
Time at Big Apple Language School	2 months	1 year	1 month	2 weeks
Distance from Big Apple Language School	1 mile	3 miles	5 miles	1/2 mile
Grade on last English test	C	A	D	B

BONUS Sample answers:
1. Tokyo is more expensive than New York.
2. American food is less spicy than Korean food.
3. Snowboarding is as easy as skiing.
4. Cats are not as friendly as dogs.

Grammar 3

2. a lot
3. more
4. like
5. from
6. much
7. many
8. as
9. similar
10. like
11. both
12. than
13. much

Unit C.3

Listening

A.

	Luis	Kate
Father is from	Colima, Mexico	Georgia
Mother is from	Colima, Mexico	Texas
Born in	San Francisco	California

B. 1. b, d   2. f   3. c, e   4. a

Vocabulary

A. 1. mountains 3. forests 5. deserts
2. oceans 4. rivers 6. beaches

Grammar 1

A.
1. the slowest; the fastest
2. the best; the hottest
3. the strangest
4. the most delicious
5. the longest; the most boring
6. the oldest, the youngest

B.
2. What's the world's busiest railway?
3. What's the world's most popular tourist spot?
4. What's the world's longest road?
5. What's the world's highest road?
6. What's the world's oldest hotel?

Grammar 2

1. ∅	5. ∅	9. ∅	13. an	17. a
2. the	6. the	10. ∅	14. a	18. the
3. ∅	7. a	11. the	15. ∅	
4. ∅	8. ∅	12. ∅	16. a	

Grammar 3

1. D (She)   2. OK   3. B (My)

Unit C.4

Listening

A. 1. What's 5. what's this
2. The what? 6. that you mix
3. that you use 7. You OK?
4. isn't it?

BONUS Sample answer:
I was surprised when I tried American cake because it is very sweet.

B. 1. fish; sea bass 4. tomatoes
2. olive 5. onions
3. lime

BONUS
Because it's a secret recipe.

Vocabulary

A. 1. a   2. f   3. b   4. e   5. c   6. d

B. 1. postcard 3. landmark 5. tour; tour
2. sightseeing 4. guidebook 6. souvenir

Grammar 1

1. what's this		**5.** What is it	
2. What's it for		**6.** What does it look like	
3. How does it work		**7.** How big is it	
4. How old is it		**8.** How much is it	

Grammar 2

A. **2.** who   **3.** that   **4.** which   **5.** who

B. **2.** Who is the person who is in charge of the other waiters in a restaurant?
    3. What is a food which is served as a starter in Italian meals?

C. **1.** c   **2.** e   **3.** a   **4.** b   **5.** d

Sample answers:
    2. Athens is the European city that hosted the 2004 Summer Olympics.
    3. J.K. Rowling is the British author who wrote the Harry Potter novels.
    4. Chinese New Year is a major holiday that is celebrated by Chinese people around the world.
    5. Aung San Suu Kyi is the Burmese leader who won the Nobel Peace Prize.

Grammar 3

2. are you	**5.** didn't you **8.** aren't we
3. won't you	**6.** was it
4. isn't it	**7.** isn't she

Unit C.5

Listening

A.
1. heard	**6.** you told
2. ever been	**7.** told
3. never been	**8.** understood
4. going to	**9.** are you
5. going to	**10.** going to be

B. **1.** d   **2.** a   **3.** b   **4.** f   **5.** c   **6.** e   **7.** g

---

Vocabulary

1. interview	**5.** job title
2. résumé	**6.** payment
3. Excellent	**7.** raise
4. hired me	**8.** reference

Grammar 1

A.
2. have known	**5.** haven't seen
3. have been	**6.** haven't gone
4. hasn't been	

B. Sample answers:
    1. I've known Bill for a long, long time.
    2. I've spoken English since I was 15 years old.
    3. I haven't eaten anything since 6 o'clock.
    4. I haven't been to Tokyo for about 2 years.

Grammar 2

A.
    1. 've seen; rented
    2. 've lived; moved
    3. bought, has/'s always liked
    4. haven't cleaned/didn't clean; haven't done
    5. have always gone; decided/'ve decided

B.
    1. have missed/missed; missed
    2. has lost/lost; left
    3. have found/found; dropped

BONUS Sample sentences:
    1. I have just made a cup of coffee.
    2. I have recently written a paper for my English class.

Grammar 3

1. become	**7.** changed
2. was	**8.** won
3. appeared	**9.** hasn't gone/didn't go
4. was	**10.** did
5. has . . . made	**11.** was playing
6. wanted	**12.** is